D. Stauffer   F. W. Hehl
V. Winkelmann   J. G. Zabolitzky

Computer Simulation and Computer Algebra

Lectures for Beginners

Second Edition

With 7 Figures

Springer-Verlag Berlin Heidelberg New York
London Paris Tokyo

Professor Dr. Dietrich Stauffer
Professor Dr. Friedrich W. Hehl
Dipl.-Phys. Volker Winkelmann*
Institut für Theoretische Physik, Universität Köln, Zülpicher Straße 77,
D–5000 Köln 41, Fed. Rep. of Germany
*Rechenzentrum, Universität Köln, Robert-Koch-Straße 10,
D–5000 Köln 41, Fed. Rep. of Germany

Professor Dr. John G. Zabolitzky
Kontron Elektronik GmbH, Breslauer Straße 2,
D–8057 Eching, Fed. Rep. of Germany

ISBN 3-540-51141-5 2. Auflage   Springer-Verlag Berlin Heidelberg New York
ISBN 0-387-51141-5 2nd edition Springer-Verlag New York Berlin Heidelberg

ISBN 3-540-18909-2 1. Auflage   Springer-Verlag Berlin Heidelberg New York
ISBN 0-387-18909-2 1st edition Springer-Verlag New York Berlin Heidelberg

2156/3150 – 543210 – Printed on acid-free paper

Preface to the Second Edition

The chapter on statistical-physics simulations has been enlarged, mainly by a discussion of multispin coding techniques for the Ising model (bit-by-bit parallel operations). In the chapter about Reduce, some details of the presentation have been corrected or clarified. The new operator MATEIGEN for the computation of eigenvectors of matrices is explained. The first chapter and the appendix remain unchanged. Needless to say, the field of computational science is advancing so quickly, for example with the development of parallel, as opposed to vectorized, algorithms, that it will not be too long before a further edition is called for.

Cologne, March 1989   *The authors*

Preface to the First Edition

Computers play an increasingly important role in many of today's activities, and correspondingly physicists find employment after graduation in computer-related jobs, often quite remote from their physics education. The present lectures, on the other hand, emphasize how we can use computers for the purposes of fundamental research in physics.

Thus we do not deal with programs designed for newspapers, banks, or travel agencies, i.e., word processing and storage of large amounts of data. Instead, our lectures concentrate on physics problems, where the computer often has to work quite hard to get a result. Our programs are necessarily quite short, excluding for example quantum chemistry programs with 10^5 program lines. The reader will learn how to handle computers for well-defined purposes. Therefore, in the end, this course will also enable him to orient himself in computer-related jobs.

The first chapter deals mainly with solutions of the Newtonian equation of motion, that force equals mass times acceleration, which is a precursor to the molecular dynamics method in statistical physics. The second chapter considers, by means of several examples, another method for statistical physics, Monte Carlo simulation. These two chapters deal with numbers, the traditional territory of computers. In contrast, analytic formula manipulation, such as $(a + 27b^3 - 4c)^5 = a^5 + 135a^4 b^3 - \ldots$, is taught in the last chapter and is important, for instance, in analytic integration or for evaluating expressions in Einstein's general theory of relativity.

All chapters try to convince readers to write their own computer programs for their own needs; it is not our aim that the reader buys software that requires the typing of only a few numbers before the results are produced, since then the students will only be amazed at the competence of the authors. Our aim is to teach them to program at least as well by themselves.

We have taught this course at various universities: repeatedly in Cologne, but also in Minneapolis and Antigonish. Prospective readers should have access to a computer (micro, mainframe, ...) to run their programs, either in batch or in interactive mode. For the first two sections, they should have about 2 years of university physics education whereas the computer algebra course can be understood by any freshman. The languages used here are Fortran, for number crunching, and Reduce, for analytic formula manipulation. Reduce is explained here in detail, and Fortran (summarized in an appendix) can be easily understood even if the reader knows only Basic or Pascal. Numerous high school students, who had never attended a university course, were able to write programs for parts of this course.

The authors come from different backgrounds (nuclear physics, solid state physics, and relativity) and have different programming styles: STRENGTH THROUGH DIVERSITY. Each author agrees, however, that the reader should not trust the advice of the other authors. We thank D. Cremer, C. Hoenselaers, T. Pfenning and W. Weiss for their help in the course and H. Quevedo for TEX-assistance. The Eden clusters in the cover picture were produced by R. Hirsch.

Cologne, April 1988   *D. Stauffer, F.W. Hehl*
                                    V. Winkelmann, J.G. Zabolitzky

Contents

4. **Appendix: A Short Introduction to FORTRAN**

1. Computational Methods in Classical Physics

John G. Zabolitzky, KONTRON Electronics, 8057 Eching, West Germany

1.1 Preface

It is the aim of this chapter to enable the readers to implement solutions to problems in the physical sciences with a computer program, and carry out the ensuing computer studies. They will therefore be shown a few basic numerical methods, and the general spirit for mapping physics problems onto a computational algorithm. It is advisable to spend some time actually implementing the exercises proposed, since is only by so doing that one may learn about, and get a feel for, the spirit of scientific computing. Examples are given using the FORTRAN 77 language and the UNIX operating system. The graphics interface used is that of the SUN workstation.

1.2 Motion of a Classical Point–Like Particle

The first few examples will deal with problems in classical Newtonian mechanics, in particular with the motion of a single classical point–like particle, described by Newton's law,

$$\mathbf{F} = m\mathbf{a} \qquad (\text{Force} = \text{mass} * \text{acceleration}). \tag{1}$$

$\mathbf{F}$ and $\mathbf{a}$ may be taken to have the dimensions of the system under consideration, i.e., if the particle is moving in three–dimensional space, $\mathbf{F}$ and $\mathbf{a}$ will be three–vectors, and the particle coordinates are labelled $\mathbf{r}$. The derivatives of these coordinates with respect to time are

$$\text{velocity:} \qquad \mathbf{v} = \frac{d\mathbf{r}}{dt} , \tag{2}$$

$$\text{acceleration:} \qquad \mathbf{a} = \frac{d^2\mathbf{r}}{dt^2} = \frac{d\mathbf{v}}{dt} . \tag{3}$$

The force $\mathbf{F}$ of (1) is the total force acting on the particle, that is the (vector) sum of all individual forces acting on the particle. Some examples of such individual forces are

$$\text{constant gravitational field} \qquad \mathbf{F} = m\mathbf{g} , \tag{4}$$

$$\text{general gravitational field} \qquad \mathbf{F} = \nabla\Phi(r_{12}) , \tag{5}$$

$$\text{potential } \Phi = G\frac{m_1 m_2}{r_{12}} , \tag{6}$$

$$\text{friction} \qquad \mathbf{F} = k\left(\frac{-\mathbf{v}}{|v|}\right) v^\alpha . \tag{7}$$

In (7) k is some suitable constant, the expression in parentheses is a unit vector in the direction opposite to the current velocity, and $v = |v| = |\mathbf{v}|$ is the magnitude of the velocity. The exponent α can take on a number of values depending upon the type of friction involved.

Equation (7) is not an exact model since the exponent should really depend on the velocity as well, though this is not considered here as the deviation is small.

Example. Let us consider the movement of a particle in constant gravitational field, (4). Using (4) in Newton's law, (1), yields

$$mg = ma \quad \text{or} \quad g = a, \tag{8}$$

which may not be too surprising. As a differential equation, (8) becomes

$$\frac{d^2\mathbf{r}}{dt^2} = g \quad \text{or} \quad \frac{d^2y}{dt^2} = -g, \quad \frac{d^2x}{dt^2} = 0, \tag{9}$$

where the coordinate vector $\mathbf{r} = (y, x)$ has been written using its two components y (elevation) and x (horizontal position).

We have now reduced the (physics) problem of calculating the motion of a point–like particle to the (mathematical) problem of solving a differential equation. In all generality, (1) may be considered as relating a known function, the force given in terms of position, velocity, acceleration etc., to the acceleration (or second derivative of the coordinate). So the general form of (1) is

$$\frac{d^2\mathbf{r}}{dt^2} = \frac{1}{m}\mathbf{F}(\mathbf{r}, \mathbf{v}, ...). \tag{10}$$

This equation does <u>not</u> specify the path, i.e. the function $\mathbf{r}(t)$, uniquely. This is because we have not specified any initial conditions, or end conditions, or boundary conditions. So far we have only specified a <u>family</u> of functions (= set of all solutions of (10) for specfic F). We need to find the number of parameters required to select one unique solution out of this set. Formally integrating (10) twice,

$$\mathbf{r}(t) = \int_{t_0}^{t} \mathbf{v}(\tau)d\tau + \mathbf{r}_0 \tag{11}$$

$$\mathbf{v}(\tau) = \frac{1}{m}\int_{\tau_0}^{\tau} \mathbf{F}(\tau')d\tau' + \mathbf{v}_0, \tag{12}$$

it is seen that we need two constant vectors, $\mathbf{r}_0$ and $\mathbf{v}_0$, to specify the solution completely, that is, initial position and initial velocity of the particle. In two dimensions, these would be four numbers, in three dimensions six. Equivalently, one could ask: What is the path terminating at a given velocity and position?, i.e, integrate backwards in time; or one could ask: What is the path passing through $\mathbf{r}_0$ at $t = 0$ and through $\mathbf{r}_1$ at $t = t_1$? This latter problem would be a boundary value problem (instead of solution and first derivative given at one point, solution given at two different points) and will be discussed in part 4 of this chapter.

Example. Continuing the above example, the solution – carrying out integrations (11) and (12) – is simple since the motion in the x and y directions is independent. The two differential equations of second order for the two scalar coordinates are [(9)]

$$\frac{d^2y}{dt^2} = -g; \quad \frac{d^2x}{dt^2} = 0. \tag{13}$$

After the first integration we have

$$\frac{dy}{dt} = v_y(t) = -gt + v_y(0); \qquad \frac{dx}{dt} = v_x(t) = v_x(0), \qquad (14)$$

with the initial conditions $v_y(0)$ and $v_x(0)$ defining the velocity vector at time $t = 0$. The second integration yields

$$y(t) = -\frac{g}{2}t^2 + v_y(0)t + y(0); \qquad x(t) = v_x(0)t + x(0). \qquad (15)$$

In (15) we have the complete solution, given the four initial conditions $x(0)$, $y(0)$, $v_x(0)$, $v_y(0)$. Here we have of course recovered the well–known fact that n differential equations of order m need $n * m$ initial conditions to have a unique solution.

In the general case (10) will not have a closed–form solution which could be derived by analytical means. Let us therefore consider numerical solution to (10). As before, I will substitute the velocities as additional variables, which yield a system of (in general coupled) differential equations of the first order:

$$\frac{d\mathbf{r}}{dt} = \mathbf{v} \qquad \text{and} \qquad \frac{d\mathbf{v}}{dt} = \frac{1}{m}\mathbf{F}(\mathbf{r}, \mathbf{v}, ...). \qquad (16)$$

For simplicity, first consider just a single equation, $y' = f(t, y)$, where the prime is shorthand for d/dt. Given y at some t_0, we want to find $y(t)$ a little time later, at $t = t_0 + \Delta t$. That is, we break the problem we want to solve (find complete path, i.e. function $y(t)$) into a number of smaller, less difficult problems: find just a little piece of the path. Furthermore, we do not require to know the path at all arbitrary points, but we ask only for the coordinates at a few selected, discrete points in time. This is the first and essential task in order to make any problem tractable numerically: we have to discretize the variables involved in the problem, here the time t. The time t will not run over a continuum of real values, but assume only values out of a given, finite set . In our case this set will be a one–dimensional mesh of time points, $\{t | t = t_0 + i\Delta t, \ i = 0, 1, 2, ..., max. \}$. By repeatedly stepping the current solution through one time interval Δt we may proceed to any finite time desired.

Given y at t_0 (that is, numbers given for these quantities), we can evaluate the function $f(t, y) = y'$ to find the value of y' at that point. We are now left with the task to extrapolate from our current knowledge about the function $y(t)$ to find the value $y(t_0 + \Delta t)$. Since $y(t)$ is the solution of a differential equation that is assumed to exist, we can also assume that $y(t)$ possesses a Taylor expansion around $t = t_0$, i.e.,

$$y(t) = y(t_0) + y'(t_0)(t - t_0) + \frac{1}{2}y''(t_0)(t - t_0)^2 + ... \qquad (17)$$

If the time step is made small enough (if $\Delta t = t - t_0$ is small enough) the second and all higher derivative terms in (17) may be neglected. In other words, in a sufficiently small neighbourhood any function may arbitrarily well be approximated by a linear function and in that case we have all the knowledge to calculate $y(t_0 + \Delta t)$:

$$y(t_0 + \Delta t) = y(t_0) + y'(t_0)\Delta t. \qquad (18)$$

This method is called the linear extrapolation or Euler method. It is quite obvious that for a finite time step Δt errors of the order Δt^2 are generated: the numerical treatment will not produce an <u>exact</u> solution, but the true solution may be approximated as well as one likes by making Δt small enough. This shows a general feature of numerical methods: the higher the accuracy desired of the results, the more computational work is required, since with smaller time steps Δt a larger number of steps are necessary to traverse a given time interval. The Euler stepping method obviously can be applied repeatedly, and we require only the initial values in order to do the first step. Errors are generated at each step and may build up as we go along. We know from (17) that errors are proportional to the second derivative of the solution – essentially the curvature. So we know where to look for problems! Wherever our final solution is to have large curvature, numerical errors may possibly have come in.

Let us now generalize the method for one function to coupled systems of differential equations like (16). At time t_0, all the right hand sides may be calculated from the known function values. The function values are known either as initial values, or from the last time step. We can therefore write down a Taylor series for <u>each</u> of the components of (16), and proceed with each component independently as we did for the single equation case. The reason is quite simple: all the couplings between the various equations are contained exclusively within the right hand sides, and are simply computed with the known values at the current time point. After that, the equations are really independent and their solution does not pose any more problems than the solution of a single equation.

Algorithm: Linear Extrapolation or Euler Method. A set of ordinary differential equations is written as

$$\frac{dy_i(t)}{dt} = f_i(t, y_1, y_2, ..., y_n), \quad i = 1, ..., n . \tag{19}$$

At an initial time $t = t_0$ all function values are provided as initial values, and the function values at time $t + \Delta t$ are calculated from

$$y_i(t + \Delta t) = y_i(t) + f_i(t, y(t)) * \Delta t, \quad i = 1, ..., n. \tag{20}$$

The method is applied repeatedly to integrate out to large times, giving as error proportional to the second derivative times Δt^2 . Two points should be noted:

1. Higher–order ordinary differential equations may be transformed into the form of (19) by substituting new variables for the higher derivatives, in exactly the same way as substituting the velocity in our physical example.
2. Quite clearly this is the simplest method possible for solving differential equations. More involved methods with higher accuracy will be discussed later.

Problem No. 1: Throw the Ball !

Consider the two–dimensional (2d) coordinate system y(up)$-x$(right). At the origin of this coordinate system a ball of mass 1kg is thrown with velocity v and angle theta with respect to ground. Gravitational acceleration is taken to be 10 m/sec^2 and the frictional force due to movement in a viscous medium is given by

$$kv^{1.87}, \quad \text{with} \quad k = 0.5 \text{ kg/sec (m/sec)}^{-0.87} .$$

<u>Where is the ball at $t = 2$ sec</u> it is thrown with a velocity of 70 m/sec at an angle of 44 degrees ? (Hint: use <u>smaller</u> v first!) Write a subroutine to calculate the path of flight. The subroutine is to be called with three arguments:

```
subroutine nstep (dt, n, y) ,
dimension y (4, n) ,
```

where dt is the timestep to be used and n is the number of timesteps to be taken plus one. The array y holds initial conditions as well as the solution, so that y (all, 1) are the initial conditions, y(all, 2) are positions and velocities after one timestep, ..., y(all, n) are positions and velocities after (n-1) timesteps. The four components are then assigned as

$y(1,t) = $ y-coordinate $y(2,t) = $ x-coordinate
$y(3,t) = $ y-velocity $ = y'$ $y(4,t) = $ x-velocity $ = x'$.

Use the linear extrapolation method to obtain the trajectory of the ball.

Input: dt, n, y(all, 1) (corresponding to t=0)
Output: y(all, 2...n)   (corresponding to t=dt,...,(n-1)*dt)

Theory.
We have Newton's law, $\mathbf{F} = m\mathbf{a}$. Acceleration a is the second derivative of the coordinates with respect to time, $\mathbf{a} = \mathbf{x}''$. We therefore have

$$\frac{d^2\mathbf{x}}{dt^2} = \frac{1}{m}[-mg\mathbf{e}_y - kv^{1.87}\mathbf{e}_v],$$

where x is a $2d$ vector of current position, the left hand side is therefore the $2d$ acceleration vector, m is the mass of the ball, g is the gravitational acceleration, $\mathbf{e}_y$ is a unit vector in the y direction, k is the constant of friction, v is the magnitude of the current velocity, and $\mathbf{e}_v$ is the unit vector in the direction of current velocity. The first term in brackets is the gravitational term, the second term comes from the friction. The direction of the gravitational force is in the negative y direction, the direction of the frictional force is opposite to that of the velocity.

Implementation.
Using the above constants and equation, it is straightforward to write down the right hand side of the derivative vector, $y' = ..., x' = ..., y'' = ..., x'' = ...$ as derivatives of y, x, y', x'. We therefore have the problem in the canonical form and can use the algorithm given above. Collect your subroutine(s) in any file with extension .f. (e.g., myball.f). The procedure to translate, load and execute the program is execball. You therefore type "execball myball" .

```
jgz%
jgz% cat execball
f77 -o $1   -f68881 -O $1.f   /u/jgz/cpc/scaff1.o -lcore77
                              -lcore -lsunwindow -lpixrect -lm
$1
jgz%
jgz%
```

Provided Scaffold for Problem # 1.

```
      subroutine init (dt,y,tmax,nmax,n)
      dimension y(4)
c
c this subroutine initializes the ball fly problem
```

```
c     by obtaining user input
c
    2 write (*,*) 'enter end-time'
      read (*,*) tmax
      if (tmax .le.  0.0) then
            write (*,*) 'illegal end-time, must be > 0'
            goto 2
      endif
    1 write (*,*) 'enter time step'
      read (*,*) dt
      if (dt .le.  0.0) then
            write (*,*) 'illegal time step, must be > 0'
            goto 1
      endif
      if (dt .gt.  tmax) then
            write (*,*) 'illegal time step, > tmax'
            goto 1
      endif
      n=tmax/dt+0.1+1.
c added 1 for initial t=0 storage
      if (n .gt.  nmax) then
            write (*,*) 'too many time steps'
            goto 1
      endif
c
    3 write (*,*) 'enter velocity'
      read (*,*) v
      if (v .le.  0.0) then
            write (*,*) 'illegal velocity, must be > 0'
            goto 3
      endif
    4 write (*,*) 'enter angle in degrees'
      read (*,*) angdeg
      if (angdeg .le.  0.0 .or.  angdeg .ge.  90.0) then
            write (*,*) 'illegal angle, must be > 0 and < 90'
            goto 4
      endif
      angrad=angdeg*3.141592654/180.0
c
      y(1)=0.0
      y(2)=0.0
      y(3)=v*sin(angrad)
      y(4)=v*cos(angrad)
c
      return
      end
```

```
      program ball
c
c solves ball fly problem
c
      parameter (nmax=10000)
      dimension y(4,nmax)

c get input
    1 call init (dt,y,tmax,nmax,n)
c
c document input
      write (*,*) 'solving ball fly problem for dt=',dt
      write (*,*) '                      up to tmax=',tmax
      write (*,*) '              resulting in nsteps=',n
      write (*,*) '          for initial velocities=',y(3,1),y(4,1)
c
c call problem solution code
      call nstep (dt,n,y)
c
c write out results
      write (*,234) (n-1)*dt,(y(i,n),i=1,4)
  234 format (' at tmax=',f10.3,'   y=',f15.6,'   x=',f15.6,/,
     *          19x,            ' vy=',f15.6,' vx=',f15.6)
c
c draw graph of flight path
      call plobal (y,n)
      goto 1
      end


      subroutine plobal (y,n)
c plot results from ball problem
      dimension y(4,n),xx(10000),yy(10000)
      do 1 i=1,n
      xx(i)=y(2,i)
      yy(i)=y(1,i)
    1    continue
c call standard plotting routine to do the nitty--gritty
      call plotfu(xx,yy,n,1,1,-.5,10.5,-3.,5.)
      return
      end

jgz% cat solv1.f
      subroutine derivs (t,y,dydt)
      dimension y(4), dydt(4)
c
c this subroutine computes the right-hand- sides for
c   ball fly problem
c variables are  y(1)=y  y(2)=x  y(3)=y'  y(4)=x'
```

8

```
c r.h.s are y'=y'  x'=x'  y''=-g -y'cv**.87  x''=0 -x'cv**.87
c
c first, compute velocity
      v=sqrt(y(3)**2+y(4)**2)
      cv87=0.5*v**0.87
c
      dydt(1)=y(3)
      dydt(2)=y(4)
      dydt(3)=-10.0 -y(3)*cv87
      dydt(4)=0.0    -y(4)*cv87
c
      return
      end

      subroutine tstep (t0,dt,y0,y)
      dimension y0(4), y(4), dydt(4)
c
c this subroutine steps the vector y through one time step,
c    from t0 to t0+dt
c
      call derivs (t0,y0,dydt)
      do 1 i=1,4
    1 y(i)=y0(i)+dt*dydt(i)
c
      return
      end

      subroutine nstep (dt,n,y)
      dimension y(4,n)
c
c this subroutine solves the ball fly problem for n-1 time steps
c    given initial conditions at t=0 in y(*,1)
c
      t=0.0
      do 1 i=2,n
      call tstep (t,dt,y(1,i-1),y(1,i))
    1 t=t+dt
c
      return
      end

jgz% cat examp1.out
   solving ball fly problem for dt=    1.00000e-03
                        up to tmax=    2.000000
               resulting in nsteps=  2001
            for initial velocities=   48.62609    50.35379
   at tmax=     2.000  y=       -0.201220  x=        7.995113
                       vy=      -4.889576 vx=        0.309135
```

```
solving ball fly problem for dt=    3.00000e-04
                  up to tmax=   2.000000
           resulting in nsteps=  6667
        for initial velocities=   48.62609    50.35379
at tmax=    2.000  y=      -0.183019  x=      8.009531
                 vy=      -4.888783  vx=     0.310836
jgz%
```

It is seen clearly that the numerical result depends upon the stepsize used, as is to be expected from the previous discussion. The difference gives some indications of the numerical error in the final result.

1.3 Short Course in FORTRAN Programming Methodology

You want to obtain good solutions to a problem as fast as possible and there are a number of programming methods which will help you to do so. The most important consideration is to keep your thoughts clean, modular and hierarchical. The only way humans can solve complex problems is by means of breaking them down into smaller ones. This is applied recursively until you finally reach the level of trivialities: the problem is solved. In exactly the same way you should construct your programs: define blocks which attack a particular task. In order to solve some well–defined task, one such block will have to call upon other well–defined tasks. These blocks of work should be made into FORTRAN subroutines (or functions). As a rule no subroutine should be more than about one (with an absolute maximum of two) pages of FORTRAN. The less skilled you are, the smaller the subroutines should be. For a beginner 5–10 lines of code is a reasonable size.

One subroutine should correspond to one small, well–defined piece of work which may be trivial or elementary; in this case, we have a lowest–level subroutine in front of us which does not call any others to do some work for it. On the next level, more complex tasks may be accomplished by another small routine calling some lower–level routines to do logical pieces of work. This partitioning should be done on a basis of logical connectednes: keep things together which belong together, and do not mix together different tasks.

This information about subroutines applies equally well to data structures: the lowest level is the machine word, usually a floating–point real number or an integer. These individual objects may be grouped together into one–dimensional arrays.

```
element      array
  a(1)       dimension a(100)
  ....         do 1 i=1,100
  a(100)   1 a(i)=1./i
```

Of course, you only group together in an array data that is logically connected, like components of a vector, or values of a function at a number of points, like the $1/x$ function in above example. In the first problem the four elements of the solution vector are grouped together:

$$y, \ x, \ v_y, \ v_x \longrightarrow y(1), \ y(2), \ y(3), \ y(4).$$

At a <u>fixed</u> time t, these four data elements define a state of our system (the ball in this case).

In order to form larger blocks, we want to bundle together things which belong together. Since we are solving a differential equation in time, the sequence of solution vectors (four numbers at $t = 0$), (four numbers at $t = dt$), (four numbers at $t = 2dt$), ..., should be bound together. We achieve this by putting them into a single two–dimensional array, the columns of which are the individual solution vectors at fixed time:

$$
\begin{aligned}
y(t = 0) &= y(1,1) & y(t = dt) &= y(1,2) & \ldots & & y(t = (n-1)dt) &= y(1,n), \\
x(t = 0) &= y(2,1) & x(t = dt) &= y(2,2) & \ldots & & x(t = (n-1)dt) &= y(2,n), \\
vy(t = 0) &= y(3,1) & vy(t = dt) &= y(3,2) & \ldots & & vy(t = (n-1)dt) &= y(3,n), \\
vx(t = 0) &= y(4,1) & vx(t = dt) &= y(4,2) & \ldots & & vx(t = (n-1)dt) &= y(4,n).
\end{aligned}
$$

One should always store the lower–level entities, in our case the four–element solution vectors, as columns of larger arrays since arrays are stored by column in storage when one uses FORTRAN. The actual sequence of elements in linear address space, i.e., within the computer memory, is

$$y(1,1)\ y(2,1)\ y(3,1)\ y(4,1)\ y(1,2)\ y(2,2)\ y(3,2)\ y(4,2)\ y(1,3)\ y(2,3)...\quad .$$

A trivial example of subroutining

Now assume that we want to perform some tasks on columns of an array, for all columns within the array. Let us suppose that the task is replacing the elements within each column by their average value. There are two logically distinct operations within this problem: a) the calculation of average values; b) operating on all columns of an array. It is too complicated for us to have both things in our mind at the same time: the particular task to be performed for each dataset (column), and the organization of work for all columns. We will get confused very easily, make mistakes, etc., and it will take us a long time to arrive at a correct solution. Therefore, we break down the program into two subroutines: one for doing averages, the other one for taking care of organizational aspects.

Averages are easy (assuming length of columns = four):

```
      subroutine aver (z)          task:  do averages
      dimension z(4)               declare the data
c compute the average of z,        insert a comment so that you will
c   and store to all z elements    be able to understand this
      sum=0.0                             two years from now
      do 1 i=1,4                          (or someone else)
 1    sum=sum+z(i)                  form the sum
      av=sum/4.                     compute average
      do 2 i=1,4
 2    z(i)=av                       store average to data elements
      return                        return to caller
      end                           syntactic end of program unit
```

This subroutine has absolutely no idea if this task is to be performed just once, or many times; it does not know where the data comes from, etc. It just focusses exclusively onto a single aspect of the problem at hand: compute the average of a series of numbers, and replace the original numbers by this average.

The probem of organizing this for a number of columns is completely unrelated to the notion of an average; for details, ask a specialist. Call the subroutine. The calling routine may therefore look like

```
      subroutine smooth(u,n)        this routine needs the whole array
c smooth out the 4 components of       comment for documentation
c   each column of u.  u has n columns.
      dimension u(4,n)              declare the data
      do 1 i=1,n                    loop over individual tasks
    1 call aver (u(1,i))            do it, whatever it may be
      return                        go back to caller
      end
```

Here, we make use of a particular FORTRAN feature: passing a column out of some bigger array as a one–dimensional array to some subroutine.

Designing a program

Do not immediately run to a keyboard if you want to write a program. The first step is to sit down and think about the problem at length (and in peace). You must have the individual steps to be followed through clearly in your mind before you proceed to implement them. So first write down what needs to be done, in chronological sequence, and collect all the formulas required in the most explicit form possible. The next step is the planning of the data structures. Which information will have to be stored? How is it to be grouped together? What are suitable arrays to be defined? What will their dimensions and names be?

Another important step is the segmentation of tasks into subroutines. The first step, the planning on paper of what to do, should give you some idea about a suitable tree–structure of tasks. Remember the basic property of a subroutine: solve some small self–contained piece of the problem; call upon other subroutines to do larger blocks of well–defined work; be called upon by callers worried about more global aspects of the problem at large.

As an example, consider the scaffold provided for problem number one. The tree struc-ture of subroutines is ("sbr" is shorthand for subroutine) :

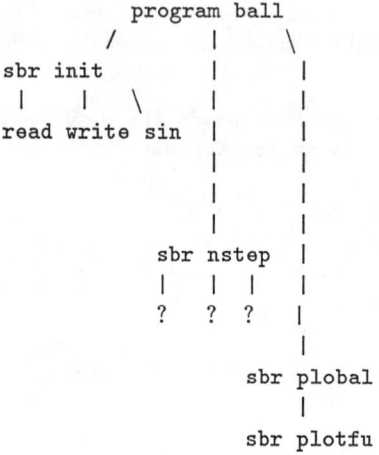

```
                program ball              solves complete ball--fly
              /     |     \                    problem
      sbr init      |      |             initializes by means of
       |   |  \     |      |             obtaining input
    read write sin  |      |             for small pieces of this:
                    |      |             read input, write request
                    |      |             and errors, sin function
                    |      |
                 sbr nstep |             solves differential eqn.
                  |  |  |  |                    for all times
                  ?  ?  ?  |             up to you. calc. r.h.s.?
                           |                  do one timestep?
                     sbr plobal          plot results of ball fly
                           |
                     sbr plotfu          general plotting routine
```

I hope that you see quite clearly the principle of division of labour among specialists: the input routine does not know anything about differential equations, the equation solver does not know anything about input/output, and nobody knows anything about graphical displays but plobal and plotfu. Subroutine plotfu is a generalist, doing all kinds of plotting tasks; plobal is a special purpose interface routine adapting the general plotfu routine to the very special task at hand here. So plobal knows about the specific display requirements of the present problem in the intervals $(-.5, 10.5)$ for the x—range and $(-3., 5.)$ for the y—range are peculiar to this case, and anticipates the possible range of solutions for the posed question. Also, some data reshuffling is done within plobal since the general–purpose plotfu routine has different conventions for data storage than are used throughout the differential equation solving, and some conversion must take place. In particular, the display need not know about the velocities, since it just plots the path; so this data is not handed over to the plotfu routine. The two parameters 1,1, just indicate that plotfu can take care of some more general displaying tasks than are required here (we will discover these uses later).

1.4 Methods of Higher Accuracy (and efficiency)

The Euler method is based on the assumption that the second derivative of the solution functions is finite (bounded), and therefore the error can be made arbitrarily small. However, it may be that in order to make practical use of this one would have to use ridiculously small increments Δt. Assuming that the higher order terms in the Taylor expansion do not matter (which can be well justified in general), at each time step an error of the order

$$\epsilon \approx \Delta t^2 * k \tag{21}$$

is introduced, where k is proportional to $y''(t)$. This is because we only approximated (17) by its first two terms. Integrating a differential equation over a fixed length T in time will require $T/\Delta t$ steps. At each step the errors may add up – we begin the second step from a slightly incorrect point, again make a slight error, and so on – so that the total error at time T is expected to be

$$\epsilon \approx \Delta t^2 * k * \frac{T}{\Delta t} = c\Delta t. \tag{22}$$

This consideration shows that the Euler method is not very efficient. In order to get a result M times more accurate, that is with an error M times smaller than a reference calculation, we need to reduce the time step by a factor of M, i.e. put in M times as much CPU time. This is about the worst possible behaviour. Only some Monte Carlo methods are worse, with an increase of work by M^2 if we want to increase the accuracy by a factor of M (such methods will be discussed later on in the book). What is highly desirable is a method where the error is proportional to some higher power of the step size than first. One says that the Euler method is a first–order method (the error in a single step is quadratic in the stepsize, and the error after integration of a fixed–length interval may be expected to be linear or first–order in the stepsize).

The essential step of arriving at the Euler method was recognition of the fact that some extrapolation scheme is needed, and using the Taylor expansion (17) in order to provide this extrapolation. The obvious improvement upon the previous procedure is to try and compensate more terms within this expansion. Unfortunately, doing so would require knowledge about higher–order derivatives of the unknown function y. Of course, the given function $f = y'$ could be formally differentiated, and the resulting expressions numerically evaluated to yield this information (so–called higher–order Taylor methods). This scheme is not very practical, however, since these expressions usually become rather unwieldy and too cumbersome to evaluate. One therefore resorts to evaluation of f at different points within the (y, t) plane in order to gain knowledge about the "landscape" the solution is supposed to move in (direction field). The information about these "surroundings" can then be used to cancel the error term, arriving at a solution accurate to one power higher than the previous method. This idea can then be iterated in order to yield expressions of arbitrary order.

There is a price to be paid, however, for cancelling a large number of error terms: one has to perform a number of evaluations of the right–hand side of function f at each time step. Since evaluation of f may be very CPU–time–consuming, one does not want to perform too many evaluations. Therefore, a few specific implementations of the previous idea – known as Runge–Kutta methods – have been used most widely and found to represent a reasonable balance between computational work and order of accuracy attained. The most frequently used version is the fourth–order Runge–Kutta method. One obtains four different values for the derivative,

$$
\begin{aligned}
k_1 &= f\left(t \quad\quad, y \quad\quad\right), \\
k_2 &= f\left(t + \frac{h}{2}, y + h\frac{k_1}{2}\right), \\
k_3 &= f\left(t + \frac{h}{2}, y + h\frac{k_2}{2}\right), \\
k_4 &= f\left(t + h, y + hk_3 \quad\right),
\end{aligned}
\tag{23}
$$

where the abbreviation h has been used for the stepsize Δt. These four expressions all represent approximations to the first derivative of $y(t)$, and for all of them we have

$$
y(t + h) = y(t) + hk_i + error_i.
\tag{24}
$$

It can be shown that the specific sum of these four approximations, given by

$$
y(t + h) = y(t) + \frac{h}{6} * (k_1 + 2k_2 + 2k_3 + k_4) + O(h^5),
\tag{25}
$$

cancels out the various error terms of (23) to order h^5 . Equation (25) together with (23) therefore represents a fourth–order approximation and is called the fourth–order Runge–Kutta method. This is one of the most widely used methods of solving ordinary differential equations.

Algorithm: Fourth–order Runge–Kutta Method. Given a set of values $y_i(t)$ at time t, evaluate in (23) all k_{1i} , then all k_{2i} , then all k_{3i} , and finally all k_{4i} from the corresponding f_i . Then, for each component separately, the solution for $t + \Delta t$ is given by adding up the linear combinations (25) (disregarding the error term, of course).

One may ask why one does not proceed to much higher order methods than this one, say 10th or 20th order. The reason is that accuracy is not the same as order: the error term not only has the factor of power h, it also has the n–th derivative of the unknown function as a factor. In many circumstances, the derivatives may grow with order (why do you think one has the $1/n!$ in the Taylor formula ?), so that for a given stepsize, a higher–order approximation may in fact be worse than a lower–order approximation! This is – apart from having to evaluate the right–hand side f too frequently – the essential reason why methods of higher–order than fourth are very seldomly used.

We are still left with the problem of choosing a proper stepsize in order to obtain a solution to the accuracy desired. So far we have been forced to use a trial–and–error scheme: try out a stepsize, try another one, and if the solution does not differ within the expected error (depending upon the order of the method used) accept the solution, otherwise, try smaller stepsizes. This may be fine for an exercise, but may become a nuisance in practical applications. One would like to have a method which chooses its own stepsize. One way to accomplish this is to simply automate the previous statement: the computer program can try out different stepsizes by itself, and choose a suitable one dynamically – that is, at some point (time) in the solution, a large stepsize may be appropriate, at other points (times) a smaller stepsize may be required. This latter requirement is quite obvious in some physics applications. Consider a space vehicle travelling through the solar system. Most of the time, the distances to all masses (planets, sun, moons, etc.,) will be large. Therefore, the gravitational field is varying only slowly. However, from time to time the space vehicle may come close to a planet where the forces will vary much more rapidly ($F \simeq 1/r^2$). This will be the case for comparatively small time intervals only, and the derivatives will be large there: a much smaller stepsize is needed here than in outer space regions. Of course, in principle one could integrate all of the flight path (another name for solving a differential equation) with a time interval of the minimal stepsize. However, this would waste enormous resources: the stepsize could be hundreds of times bigger for most of the time! That is, one may save factors of hundreds in computer time (= computing Dollars).

For a moment, let us forget about the details of our differential equations solvers. Instead just consider some algorithm which will produce an estimate of the unknown function at the next time step, of order n:

$$\text{stepsize } h \qquad \text{one step} \qquad \text{result } r_1 = y(t + h) + 1ch^{n+1}$$

$$(26)$$

$$\text{stepsize } \frac{h}{2} \qquad \text{two steps} \qquad \text{result } r_2 = y(t + h) + 2c\left(\frac{h}{2}\right)^{n+1}$$

Here we assume that the algorithm has been applied three times for a single step of size h, once with stepsize h and twice with $h/2$. The overhead factor is not three, but only 1.5 –

because comparison must be made with integrating with stepsize $h/2$, so that there is only one additional step taken. Of course the error terms are unknown in their exact values, but the constant c may be assumed to be the same in both cases, and the power of h is known. Therefore (26) are two equations with two unknowns: $y(t+h)$, and c. In other words, we may obtain an improved version of $y(t+h)$ [which actually will be accurate to one more order], as well as an estimate of the numerical error $c(h/2)^{n+1}$. We have another example of the technique of cancellation of error terms, and a general scheme to obtain error estimates by comparison of different calculations.

More specifically, assuming the fourth–order Runge–Kutta method ($n = 4$), we have the extrapolated result and assume for the error Δ (solving (26))

$$y(t + h) = r_2 + \frac{r_2 - r_1}{15},$$

$$\Delta = |r_2 - r_1|.$$

(27)

The absolute value is required because the error will be used as a positive quantity. Taking the last equation as an estimate for the numerical error in the first equation is certainly on the conservative side. Since this really is the error of the stepsize h method, a factor $1/16$ could be applied to get the error estimate for stepsize $h/2$ method and the extrapolated result. However, we should always stay on the safe side when dealing with errors. After all, it does not do any harm if the solution is a little more accurate than we think! We now want to adjust the stepsize h such that the error Δ assumes a predefined value. Whenever the measured accuracy is too high, i.e., Δ too small, we increase h in order to save computer time. Whenever the measured accuracy does not meet our standards, we decrease h in order to get a more accurate result. When this is necessary we should redo the current step, since it was not accurate enough. Let h be the stepsize currently in use, Δ the measured error from (27), and e the desired error. We then obtain a new stepsize from

$$h_{new} = 0.9h \left(\frac{e}{\Delta}\right)^{0.20} \qquad \text{if} \qquad e > \Delta,$$

$$h_{new} = 0.9h \left(\frac{e}{\Delta}\right)^{0.25} \qquad \text{if} \qquad e < \Delta.$$

(28)

The factor 0.9 indicates that we always want to be on the safe side. The difference in exponents arises from the fact that we do not know too much about the buildup of errors as we follow the path. On reducing the stepsize, we need more steps resulting in a final error proportional to the <u>fourth</u> power of the stepsize, not the fifth. Therefore equations (28) once again express our conservative desire to always stay on the safe side, and take the smaller stepsize.

The last question to be discussed in this context is the choice of desired error e. A constant relative error, $e \approx y$, is rarely useful because y may go through zero. A constant absolute error is much more reasonable in most cases, but it must be borne in mind that e is representing the error <u>at each step</u> of the solution procedure, so it should be taken conservatively small, again. If solving systems of equations, like our space vehicle example with six equations (three coordinate and three velocity), we have then to provide different accuracy levels for the different components: the absolute magnitudes of coordinates and velocities will differ in all probability, and this must be reflected in the prescribed error. We will therefore not have just just one estimate for a new stepsize from (28), but as many different estimates as there are equations. Obviously, we take the smallest of these – again we keep on the safe side by adjusting the stepsize to the most difficult component of our differential equation. One must be careful not to overdo the accuracy: one limit is set by the length of the computer word used, i.e., rounding errors due to finite precision arithmetic. We use 32 bit floating point numbers, so that the precision is limited to about one part in 10^6 . The stepsize can potentially become so small that expressions like $y = y + \Delta y$ result in the old value of y, since adding Δy could amount to adding something in the 40th digit of a 32–bit word, which obviously does not change the 32–bit word. Another danger is that the stepsize estimate may become too large, because Δ gets too small, close to machine accuracy level; one should should guard against increasing the stepsize by more than a factor of 10. Let us now collect all of the previous statements.

Algorithm: Adaptive Stepsize Control for Fourth–Order Runge–Kutta. With current stepsize h, do one Runge–Kutta integration step, yielding one estimate r_{i1} for each component. Beginning at the same old time t, do two Runge–Kutta steps with stepsize $h/2$, yielding another estimate r_{i2} for each component. Evaluate solutions at $t + h$ from (27) together with error estimates Δ_i, for each component. For each component, use (28) with the prescribed absolute error e_i to obtain a new stepsize for each component, $h_{i,new}$. The new stepsize is the minimum of these. If this minimum is smaller than the original stepsize h, redo the whole procedure. Beware of a new stepsize > 5 times the old stepsize, or the stepsize becoming so small that no further changes result to either the t or the y variables!

Two more methods are in general use to solve systems of ordinary differential equations: Predictor–Corrector methods, and extrapolation methods, e.g., Bulirsch–Stoer. In any case, we know that we have to accumulate more knowledge about the functions f and/or y. In the Runge–Kutta method we obtained that knowledge by probing f at a number of different places. In Predictor–Corrector methods, one uses more information about y, not only y at the last time step is used, but also at two, three,..., timesteps back. One may then use a higher–order polynomial to extrapolate this sequence of points just one time step ahead, the predictor step. Function values obtained in this way are used as arguments of the right–hand sides f, and the derivatives $y' = f(t, y)$ can be calculated. Finally, the derivatives are integrated to yield an improved estimate for y (the corrector step).

Extrapolation methods, and in particular the method by Bulirsch and Stoer, are for most applications the most accurate and most efficient algorithms, though a little more involved than the Runge–Kutta discussed above. Here additional knowledge is obtained by doing a number of independent calculations for a larger interval, say calculate $y(T)$. These calculations are done with a number of different step sizes h, so that the total of all these results is given by $y(T, h)$. One may then use some extrapolation technique in order to extrapolate to $h = 0$. In this way, one probes the function f in many ways, and tries to obtain knowledge about y over a macroscopic regime. Given a number of measurements (a number of different results for different h) extrapolation is a powerful tool to obtain high–precision final results for $y(T)$.

One general remark about computer experiments: whenever we do a calculation we should incorporate as many tests and measurements as possible – in order to learn as much as we can. The adaptive step–size control is one example. Phyics problems usually provide us with a few more tests we can make. If we are integrating a Newtonian system with conservative forces (that is, without friction and only gradients of potentials as forces, like in the gravitational case), there are constants of the motion: total energy, total angular momentum and total momentum in some cases. A possible test for an accurate solution is evaluation of the energy as we go along, or at the initial and final positions. Since we <u>know</u> that the energy is a constant of the motion, the calculation must bear this out if accurate.

Problem No. 2: Space Travel.

Consider a two−dimensional ($2D$) $x - y$ coordinate system. At a number of points (x_i, y_i) there are some masses m_i, $i = 1, 2, ..., N$. These masses are <u>fixed</u> at their respective locations and cannot move. A space vehicle appears at time $t = 0$, position (x_0, y_0), and velocity (v_{x_0}, v_{y_0}). Calculate the flight path of the vehicle. Units are such that the gravitational constant $G = 1$. In particular, for $N = 4$, with masses of 100 units each at positions (3,3), (5,5), (7,7) and (9,9), as initial position (0,0); initial velocity 4 at an angle of 17.5 degrees, where is the space vehicle, and what is its velocity vector, at time $t = 6$? This is not too difficult. As an exercise investigate the same question at time $t = 11$! (which is quite a bit more difficult). You could also assure yourself that you <u>cannot</u> answer the question at $t = 15$! Why ?

Write a subroutine <u>to do one time−step</u> by means of the fourth−order Runge− Kutta method. <u>An optional, but recommended,</u> task is to use adaptive stepsize control; do the calculation three times with three different programs: with the Euler method from the previous problem, Runge−Kutta without, and with adaptive stepsize control. You will then see the increasing efficiency. Without adaptive time step control, you will not be able to proceed to $t = 11$.

```
subroutine step1 (y,h,t, yout,hout,tout)
dimension y(4),yout(4)
common /masses/ nmass,xym(3,10)
common /errors/ err(4)
```

Input: y, the four components (same sequence as first problem) at time t
      h, the suggested stepsize to use
      t, the time at which y is given
Output:yout, the four components after a timestep
      hout, the timestep to be used next time around (=h if no adaptive
        stepsize control is used)
      tout, the time at which yout has been calculated. Without adaptive
        stepsize control this will be =t+h, with it might be smaller.
Constant data in common blocks:
    nmass, the number of masses present
    xym(1,i), x-coordinates of masses

    xym(2,i), y-coordinates of masses   } i=1,..., nmass

    xym(3,i), m, the value of the mass at that point
    err(1...4), the desired errors for the four solution components
Recall the component sequence from first problem: 1=y, 2=x, 3=v$_y$, 4=v$_x$.

Theory. The force acting upon our space vehicle is given by the sum of individual gravitational terms, (carry out the gradient in (5))

$$\mathbf{F} = \sum_i \frac{-Gmm_i\mathbf{r}_i}{r_i^3},$$

where m is the mass of the space vehicle, and $\mathbf{r}_i = (x,y) - (x_i,y_i)$ is the distance vector between the space vehicle and fixed mass number i. Because of

$$\frac{d^2\mathbf{r}}{dt^2} = \frac{1}{m}\mathbf{F}$$

the mass of the space vehicle drops out and need not be known. The force is divergent at small distances. Is this related to the numerical problems ?

Implementation suggestions: Write a subroutine to calculate the right−hand sides, f_i, $i = 1, 2, 3, 4$. This will be the same for all methods. Write a subroutine to do one Runge−Kutta step with fixed stepsize dt. Call this subroutine three times to do the adaptive stepsize control. Beware of too small or too large step sizes, as discussed above!

```
cat scaff2.f
        function energy (y)
        dimension y(4)
        common /masses/ nmass,xym(3,10)
c calculates the total energy of particle, first kinetic, add potential
c N.B. vehicle mass scales out as some constant factor
        e=0.5*(y(3)**2+y(4)**2)
        do 1 i=1,nmass
    1   e=e-xym(3,i)/sqrt((xym(1,i)-y(2))**2+(xym(2,i)-y(1))**2)
        energy=e
        return
        end
        subroutine getmas (xym,n)
        parameter (nmax=10)
        dimension xym(3,nmax)
        data b/10.0/
c
c get masses from operator
c
        n=0
    1   write (*,*) 'enter x,y,mass (0=done)'
        read (*,*) x,y,am
        if (am .eq.  0.0) return
c
        if (x .lt.  0.  .or.  x .gt.  b .or.
    *        y .lt.  0.  .or.  y .gt.  b)       then
            write (*,*) 'x,y outside range 0,',b
```

```
              goto 1
        endif
        if (am .lt.  0.0) then
              write (*,*) 'no negative mass exists'
              goto 1
        endif
        if (am .gt.  500.)  then
              write (*,*) 'no mass > 500 please'
              goto 1
        endif
        n=n+1
        xym(1,n)=x
        xym(2,n)=y
        xym(3,n)=am
c
c display this placement
        call dismas (x,y,am)
        if (n .eq.  nmax) return
        goto 1
        end
        subroutine dismas (x,y,f)
c display blob of area f at x,y
        dimension xx(50),yy(50)
        data m/50/,pi/3.141592654/
c for circle drawing
        rr=f*0.001
        if (rr .gt.  1.)  rr=1.
        r=sqrt(rr)
        do 1 i=1,m
        phi=i*2.*pi/m
        xx(i)=r*sin(phi)+x
    1   yy(i)=r*cos(phi)+y
c select shady pattern
        call SetFillIndex(245)
        call PolygonAbs2(xx,yy,m)
        return
        end
        program move2d
c particle movement in 2d pot landscape
      dimension y(4),yout(4)
        common /masses/ nmass,xym(3,10)
        common /errors/ err(4)
        logical flag
c flag signals last timestep
c
c initialize display area
        call plotfu (xym,xym,0,0,1, -1.5,13.5, -2.5,13.5)
```

```
c
c get mass distribution
        call getmas (xym,nmass)
c
c
c get initial conditions etc.
    1 call init (dt,y,tmax,eps)
c
c compute and print starting energy, for check of accuracy
        e=energy(y)
        n=tmax/dt+.99
c
        write (*,*) 'solve 2d particle problem for dt=',dt
        write (*,*) '                        up to tmax=',tmax
        write (*,*) '                 resulting in nsteps=',n
        write (*,*) '   with overall accuracy epsilon=',eps
        write (*,*) '            for initial velocities=',y(3),y(4)
        write (*,*) '               initial total energy=',e
c
        t=0.0
        flag=.false.
c now do next timestep; first set desired errors
  200   do 201 i=1,4
        e=abs(y(i))
        if (e .lt.  1.)  e=1.
        err(i)=e*eps
  201   continue
        call step1 (y,dt,t,  yout,dtout,tout)
c update display
        call plpath(y,yout,t,tout)
c make old point = new point
        do 220 i=1,4
  220   y(i)=yout(i)
        dt=dtout
        t=tout
c next step ?
        if (flag) goto 300
        if (t .lt.  tmax-dt) goto 200
        dt=tmax-t
        flag=.true.
        goto 200
c
c compute and print final energy.  if accurate, should be = initial
  300     e=energy(y)
        write (*,*) '                 final total energy=',e
        write (*,234) t,(y(i),i=1,4)
  234 format (' at tmax=',f10.3,'  y=',f15.6,'  x=',f15.6,/,
```

```
      *           19x,                  ' vy=',f15.6,' vx=',f15.6)
        goto 1
        end
          subroutine plpath(yi,yo,t,tout)
          dimension yi(4),yo(4)
c plot (=display) segment of path
          character*2 tnum
c
          call MoveAbs2(yi(2),yi(1))
          call LineAbs2(yo(2),yo(1))
c find if integer time value within this interval
          it0=t
          it1=tout
          if (it0 .ne.  it1) then
                  write (tnum,2) it1
     2            format (i2)
                  call text (tnum)
          endif
          return
          end
        subroutine init (dt,y,tmax,eps)
        dimension y(4)
c
c this subroutine initializes the ball fly problem
c   by obtaining user input
c
      2 write (*,*) 'enter end-time'
        read (*,*) tmax
        if (tmax .le.  0.0) then
              write (*,*) 'illegal end-time, must be > 0'
              goto 2
        endif
      1 write (*,*) 'enter time step'
        read (*,*) dt
        if (dt .le.  0.0) then
              write (*,*) 'illegal time step, must be > 0'
              goto 1
        endif
        if (dt .gt.  tmax) then
              write (*,*) 'illegal time step, > tmax'
              goto 1
        endif
c
      7 write (*,*) 'enter accuracy epsilon'
        read (*,*) eps
        if (eps .lt.  1.e-6) then
                  write (*,*) 'eps too small, must be >= 1e-6'
```

```fortran
                goto 7
          endif
c user must make shure eps is not too large for his problem !!!
c
      3 write (*,*) 'enter velocity'
        read (*,*) v
        if (v .le.  0.0) then
               write (*,*) 'illegal velocity, must be > 0'
               goto 3
        endif
      4 write (*,*) 'enter angle in degrees'
        read (*,*) angdeg
        angrad=angdeg*3.141592654/180.0
c
        y(1)=0.0
        y(2)=0.0
        y(3)=v*sin(angrad)
        y(4)=v*cos(angrad)
c
        return
        end
c     ============================================================
          subroutine plotfu (x,y,n,m,ny1dim, xmin,xmax, ymin,ymax)
          dimension x(n),y(ny1dim,m)
c plot a set of m functions, with axis labelling
c clip at xmin,xmax, ymin,ymax; x assumed monotonic.
          include ''/usr/include/f77/usercore77.h"
          integer vsurf(VWSURFSIZE),locptr(2)
          character* 32    locstring(4)
          integer pixwindd,InitializeCore,InitializeVwsurf,SelectVwsurf
          external pixwindd
          save kode
          data kode/0/
          data vsurf/VWSURFSIZE*0/
          data locstring/"000,000,600,400,000,0,100,100,0,",
      *               "600,000,600,400,200,0,100,100,0,",
      *               "000,450,600,400,400,0,100,100,0,",
      *               "600,450,600,400,600,0,100,100,0,"/
          if (kode .eq.  0) then
          kode=1
          if (InitializeCore(DYNAMICA,NOINPUT,TWOD) .ne.  0) call exit(1)
          do 22 i=1,VWSURFSIZE
 22       vsurf(i)=0
          vsurf(DDINDEX)=loc(pixwindd)
c set vsurf.flags to new_window
          vsurf(20)=1
c set pointer to location pointer
```

```
c          vsurf(21)=loc(locptr)
c          locptr(1)=loc(locstring(kode))
c          locptr(2)=0
c
           CALL SETNDCSPACE2 (1.0,1.0)
           call SetViewPort2 (0.,1.,0.,1.)
c
           if (InitializeVwsurf(vsurf,FALSE) .ne.  0) call exit(2)
           if (SelectVwsurf(vsurf) .ne.  0) call exit(3)
           call SetWindow(xmin,xmax,ymin,ymax)
ccc        call SetImgXformType(XFORM2)
ccc        call SetImgTransform2(1.,4./3.,0.,0.,0.)
cxcx       call CreateRetainSeg(kode)
           call CreateTempSeg
           if (xmin .le.  0.  .and.  xmax .ge.  0.)  then
                   call yaxis (ymin,ymax)
           endif
           if (ymin .le.  0.  .and.  ymax .ge.  0.)  then
                   call xaxis (xmin,xmax)
           endif
           endif
c
c only create window and axes ???
           if (n .le.  0 .or.  m .le.  0) return
c          call setlineindex(kode*64-1)
c          call setlinestyle(kode-1)
c          kode=kode+1
           do 200 k=1,m
           call moveabs2(x(1),y(1,k))
           call PolylineAbs2(x,y(1,k),n)
  200      continue
c          call CloseRetainSeg()
c          call DeselectVwSurf(vsurf)
           return
           end
           subroutine xaxis (xmin,xmax)
           character*4 xnum
           call moveabs2(xmin,0.)
           call lineabs2(xmax,0.)
           ixmin=xmin
           ixmax=xmax
           do 1 ix=ixmin,ixmax
           x=ix
           call moveabs2(x,0.)
           call lineabs2(x,-.1)
           write (xnum,2) ix
    2      format (i4)
```

```
          call moveabs2(x-.4,-.2)
          call text (xnum)
     1    continue
          return
          end
          subroutine yaxis (ymin,ymax)
          character*4 ynum
          call moveabs2(0.,ymin)
          call lineabs2(0.,ymax)
          iymin=ymin
          iymax=ymax
          do 1 iy=iymin,iymax
          y=iy
          call moveabs2(0.,y)
          call lineabs2(-.1,y)
          write (ynum,2) iy
     2    format (i4)
          call moveabs2(-1.2,y)
          call text (ynum)
     1    continue
          return
          end
jgz%
cat solv2.f
          subroutine derivs (t,y,dydt)
          dimension y(4), dydt(4)
          common /masses/ nmass,xym(3,10)
c
c this subroutine computes the right-hand sides for
c    2d particle movement problem
c variables are  y(1)=y  y(2)=x  y(3)=y'  y(4)=x'
c r.h.s are y'=y'  x'=x'  y'', x''= sum gravitational forces
c
          fx=0.
          fy=0.
          do 1 i=1,nmass
          delx=xym(1,i)-y(2)
          dely=xym(2,i)-y(1)
          rm3=(delx**2+dely**2)**(-1.5)
          fx=fx+xym(3,i)*delx*rm3
     1    fy=fy+xym(3,i)*dely*rm3
c
          dydt(1)=y(3)
          dydt(2)=y(4)
          dydt(3)=fy
          dydt(4)=fx
c
```

```
      return
      end
      subroutine step1 (y0,dtin,t0,  y,dtout,tout)
      dimension y0(4), y(4), r1(4),r2(4),tmp(4),del(4)
      common /errors/ err(4)
      logical change
c
c this subroutine steps the vector y0 through one time step,
c    from t0 to t0+dt.    This version
c    ******  with adaptive stepsize control ******
c
      dt=dtin
c come to 9 if must repeat this step
    9   dt2=dt/2.
      t1=t0+dt2
      if (t1 .eq.  t0) goto 999
      call rk4 (y0 ,dt ,t0, r1)
      call rk4 (y0 ,dt2,t0, tmp)
      call rk4 (tmp,dt2,t1, r2)
      tout=t0+dt
      dtout=10000.0
      change=.false.
      do 1 i=1,4
c compute error
      del(i)=r2(i)-r1(i)
c compute extrapolated result, one order more
      y(i)=r2(i)+del(i)/15.
c check if stepsize not too small
      if (y(i) .ne.  y0(i)) change=.true.
c get new stepsize estimate
      if (del(i) .eq.  0.)  goto 1
      hnew=abs(err(i)/del(i))
      if (hnew .gt.  1.)  then
           hnew=hnew**0.20
      else
           hnew=hnew**0.25
      endif
      hnew=hnew*0.9*dt
      if (hnew .lt.  dtout) dtout=hnew
    1   continue
      if (.not.  change) goto 999
      if (dtout .lt.  dt) then
           dt=dtout
           goto 9
      endif
c close to machine word accuracy level, may estimate h=infinity.
c    avoid unreasonably large hout.
```

```fortran
        if (dtout .gt.  5.*dt) dtout=5.*dt
        return
c
c error message if eps too small:  no change with this stepsize
  999   write (*,*) 'eps is too small, single-precision no good'
        stop
        end
        subroutine rk4 (y0,dt,t0,  y)
      dimension y0(4), y(4), dydt(4), dydt2(4),dydt3(4),dydt4(4),
     *           ytry(4)
c
c this subroutine steps the vector y0 through one fourth-order
c  Runge-Kutta step, from t0 to t0+dt.c
c
        hh=dt*0.5
        h6=dt/6.
        call derivs(t0,y0,dydt)
c first step
        do 11 i=1,4
   11   ytry(i)=y0(i)+hh*dydt(i)
        th=t0+hh
        call derivs(th,ytry,dydt2)
c second step
        do 12 i=1,4
   12   ytry(i)=y0(i)+hh*dydt2(i)
        call derivs(th,ytry,dydt3)
c third step
        do 13 i=1,4
   13   ytry(i)=y0(i)+dt*dydt3(i)
        call derivs(t+dt,ytry,dydt4)
c final result calculation
        do 14 i=1,4
   14   y(i)=y0(i)+h6*(dydt(i)+dydt4(i)+2.*(dydt2(i)+dydt3(i)))
        return
        end
jgz%
```

```
jgz%
cat output2
```

```
    solve 2d particle problem for dt=    0.100000
                        up to tmax=    15.00000
                   resulting in nsteps=   150
      with overall accuracy epsilon=    1.00000e-06
              for initial velocities=    1.202823    3.814868
                 initial total energy=  -47.67063
                   final total energy=  -47.59777
at tmax=    15.000  y=       6.951267 x=       3.168372
                   vy=     -10.129745 vx=       3.470588
```

This is the most difficult case.
The requested accuracy of 1e-6 is
the highest possible with 32-bit
arithmetic. The initial conditions
are varied slightly by varying the
size of the first step taken (dt
initial value; is readjusted in first
step by automatic procedure).

```
    solve 2d particle problem for dt=    1.00000e-02
                 initial total energy=  -47.67063
                   final total energy=  -47.54682
at tmax=    15.000  y=       8.789311 x=       9.086155
                   vy=       7.234674 vx=      29.388420
```

```
    solve 2d particle problem for dt=    1.000000
                 initial total energy=  -47.67063
                   final total energy=  -47.29255
at tmax=    15.000  y=      11.585136 x=       7.078432
                   vy=       4.900776 vx=      -6.091509
```

It is seen that the energy conservation
is good to about 1% or better – but
this is by no means good enough to
provide an accurate flight path. The
coordinates and velocities vary all
over the place, and no definite answer
can be obtained. One m u s t use
double precision arithmetic to solve
this problem – which we are not
intending to do. Even in double
precision, the problem will only be
pushed to somewhat larger times, it
will always recur eventually.

```
    solve 2d particle problem for dt=    1.00000e-03
                 initial total energy=  -47.67063
                   final total energy=  -47.70902
at tmax=    15.000  y=       6.885458 x=       3.011815
                   vy=       9.854307 vx=      -3.682477
```

```
    solve 2d particle problem for dt=    0.100000
                 initial total energy=  -47.67063
                   final total energy=  -47.59333
at tmax=    11.000  y=       9.156343 x=      12.222279
                   vy=      -5.368358 vx=       3.927579
```

This is the a little simpler case
of tmax=11. Energy conservation is
not much better than at t=15; all
of the problematics come from the
close collision with the mass at (3,3)
at time approx. 7.5. But since we do no
come close to another mass again, the
error has not yet been amplified another

```
    solve 2d particle problem for dt=    1.00000e-02
                 initial total energy=  -47.67063
                   final total energy=  -47.54754
at tmax=    11.000  y=       7.841234 x=      12.285086
                   vy=      -6.252029 vx=       2.297748
```

time. The reson is of course the high
curvature at the close encounter, i.e.
the singularity in the potential or,
consequently, in the force 1/r**2.

```
    solve 2d particle problem for dt=    1.000000
                 initial total energy=  -47.67063
                   final total energy=  -47.68734
at tmax=    11.000  y=      11.271933 x=      11.146914
                   vy=      -2.393134 vx=       6.039363
```

Because of this, all higher derivatives
become large as well, making any method
unaccurate – independent of order.

```
    solve 2d particle problem for dt=    1.00000e-03
                 initial total energy=  -47.67063
                   final total energy=  -47.70936
at tmax=    11.000  y=       8.491718 x=      12.323996
                   vy=      -5.855905 vx=       3.011898
```

```
solve 2d particle problem for dt=    0.100000
            initial total energy=  -47.67063
            final total energy=  -47.67074
at tmax=    6.000  y=        2.089369  x=        10.099595
                   vy=       -5.447434 vx=        0.096269

solve 2d particle problem for dt=    1.00000e-02
            initial total energy=  -47.67063
            final total energy=  -47.67100
at tmax=    6.000  y=        2.087664  x=        10.096528
                   vy=       -5.449095 vx=        0.092138

solve 2d particle problem for dt=    1.000000
            initial total energy=  -47.67063
            final total energy=  -47.67080
at tmax=    6.000  y=        2.092861  x=        10.105886
                   vy=       -5.443902 vx=        0.104669
solve 2d particle problem for dt=    1.00000e-03
            initial total energy=  -47.67063
            final total energy=  -47.67065
at tmax=    6.000  y=        2.088028  x=        10.097003
                   vy=       -5.449006 vx=        0.092937
jgz%
```

This is the easy case of tmax=6.
Energy is conserved almost to machine
accuracy – there has not (yet) been
any close encounter of one of the
masses, no large second or higher
derivatives have been seen. In other
words, we have not (yet) come close to
any of the singularities in the force
function. Irrespective of small
variations in the initial step, we
always end up at about the same
place and with the same velocities,
to a few percent. But already here you
see the buildup of errors: each step
is accurate to machine precision,
but many errors of 1e-6 still add up!

General lesson: beware of singularities!
Whenever possible, try to treat
them by analytical methods first.

1.5 Finding Extremal Points of Motion

Consider a single classical particle within a spherical potential, $v(r)$, centered at the origin of the coordinate system. By means of the methods of the previous lectures we could obtain the path of the particle, given initial conditions (with the program of problem $\#$ 2 we can do this without any modification by simply assuming only one mass; I recommend that you experiment with this case a little (Kepler problem)). However, let me assume that we are not interested in all of the path, but just in the two questions: how close does the particle ever get to the center, and what is the largest distance it will ever achieve (if it is bound and will not go off to infinity) ?

In order to answer these questions we do not need to know any particular path, we do not even need to know the complete initial conditions. We simply make use of energy conservation: The total energy is a constant of the motion, since the forces are derived from a potential (gradient of the potential). Therefore, we need to know only the initial total energy of the particle, which is of course the initial kinetic energy plus the initial potential energy. We may then ask at which points the kinetic energy becomes zero, i.e., the total energy equals the kinetic energy. If the particle were to go beyond this point, the potential energy would be larger than the total energy, which is impossible since the kinetic energy is always positive, and therefore the sum cannot be conserved.

Let me illustrate these remarks with a particular example. Consider the classical so−called 6−12 potential,

$$v(r) = 4\epsilon \left[\left(\frac{\sigma}{r} \right)^{12} - \left(\frac{\sigma}{r} \right)^{6} \right] . \tag{29}$$

This potential describes to some accuracy the interaction between certain atoms (e.g., Argon atoms within Argon gas or liquid Argon), i.e., gives the potential energy between two atoms a distance r apart. ϵ and σ are positive parameters; σ is some typical length and ϵ an energy. A plot of $v(r)$ is shown in Fig. 1.

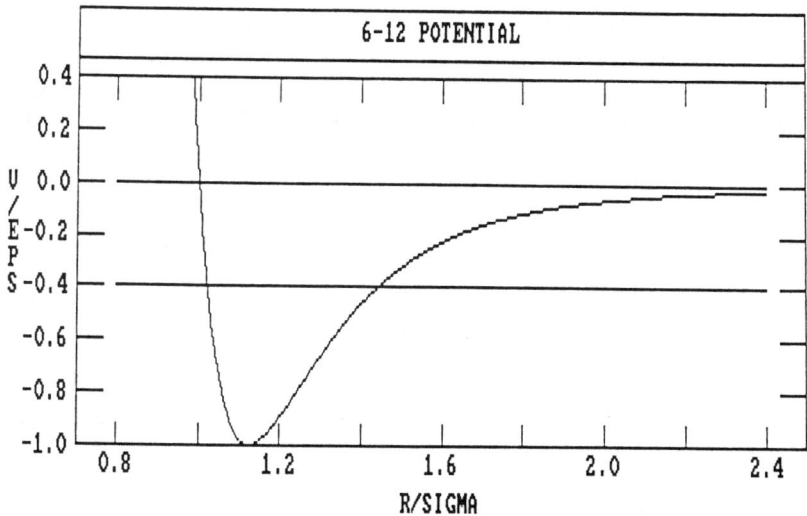

It is customary to use "reduced" units of length and energy, scaled by the two parameters of the potential. In these units, $v = 0$ at $r = 1$, v has a minimum of $v = -1$ at $r = 2^{1/6} \approx 1.12246$, and $v \rightarrow 0$ for $r \rightarrow \infty$. For $r < 1$, the potential diverges rapidly as r approaches zero. This is an expression of the quantum— mechanical Pauli exclusion principle for Fermions (in this case electrons): the electrons within atoms do not like to be pushed into each other. The attractive term is nothing but the mutual polarization of two charge densities and can be calculated from classical electrodynamics.

Assume now that a particle (in this case another atom) has total energy of -0.4 reduced units (-0.4ϵ absolute). This particle is known to be bound; therefore it cannot escape to $r = \infty$, because there $v = 0$, and the kinetic energy cannot be -0.4 reduced units. The energy conservation law does not allow this escape. The particle, by the same token, cannot get to $r \leq 1$ in reduced units ($r \leq \sigma$ absolute) since there $v \geq 0$. So the particle is confined to a finite interval of distances r, and we could try to calculate this interval from the energy conservation law alone, without recourse to any equation of motion, like Newton's law.

The total energy is shown in Fig. 1. as a straight line at -0.4. It should be obvious by now that the allowed range of r's is that range where $v(r) \leq -0.4$. Within this range the kinetic energy is non—negative, that is positive or zero. The two points where the kinetic energy is exactly equal to zero are called the classical turning points (consider the turning points of a pendulum). It is the location of these turning points that we wish to determine, i.e., we want to solve the equation

$$v(r) = E \qquad \text{or} \qquad v(r) - E = 0 \qquad \text{or} \qquad f(r) = 0 \,, \tag{30}$$

where E is the given total energy. We are therefore concerned with the problem of finding the two roots of a nonlinear equation.

With the precise form of $v(r)$ given above, this is rather trivial using the substitution

$$z = r^{-6} \longrightarrow z^2 - z + 0.1 = 0 \,, \tag{31}$$

with the solutions $r_1 \approx 1.020129$ and $r_2 \approx 1.438837$. However, more refined approximations to atomic interactions lead to much more complicated forms for the potential than (29), where closed—form solutions are not possible. Let us therefore pretend that we do not know how to solve (30) by simple means, and formulate instead a solution using a computer.

The first step in any computer study is that you should form some rough idea of what is going on. In the present case, this is exactly what we have done so far. We have convinced ourselves, essential by graphic means (i.e., plotting the functions involved), that there exist two well—isolated solutions to (30). We can give bounding intervals easily: the first solution must be within $[1, 1.2]$ and the second one within $[1.4, 1.6]$. We know beforehand that both of these intervals contain exactly one solution. This kind of information should be ascertained whenever possible before trying some automatic algorithm to find the root with higher precision. This is because multiple roots may be difficult to detect, and some roots may go unnoticed if too close to each other. Furthermore, the maxima and/or minima which arise with necessity in between roots can severely foul up some root— finders (see below). Therefore, whenever possible, try to find intervals that bound a single root before going ahead.

One of the most stable numerical algorithms is the method of bisection for finding zeroes of a function of a real variable. The idea is quite straightforward:

Algorithm: Method of bisection. Given a root bounding interval $[a, b]$, i.e., given a sign change of $f(x)$ between $x = a$ and $x = b$, evaluate $f(z)$ at $z = (a + b)/2$, i.e., in the middle of the interval. If the sign of $f(z)$ is the same as that of $f(a)$, the root is now located within $[z, b]$. If the sign of $f(z)$ is the same as that of $f(b)$, the root is now located within $[a, z]$. In any case the width of the interval has been halved. Iterate this method until the desired accuracy is achieved.

There are several remarks to be noted: 1) if there are several roots within the initial interval, exactly one of these will be found; 2) if there is <u>no</u> root within the initial interval, but a sign change due to a singularity like $1/x$, the location of the singularity will be found; 3) if the function $f(x)$ is discontinuous, i.e., has a step across $f = 0$ at some point within this interval, the position of the step will be found; 4) the method may be used to determine the position of the root <u>accurate to the last bit</u> within the machine word. There is <u>no</u> roundoff or other numerical error (apart from possible errors in the calculation of $f(x)$ itself).

This last observation gives us an excuse to consider in some more detail the representation of numbers within the computer. For integer numbers there is no problem: integers are represented in base-2 notation and 2$-$complement, i.e., the unique representation of 0 is a machine word with all bits $= 0$, and the number -1 is represented by all bits $= 1$. The only limitation is the finite size of the machine word, limiting the range of representable integers. For a 32$-$bit machine word, if bits are numbered from right (0) to left (31), one usually has bit # 31 as the sign bit, and 31 bits are used for the magnitude. Then, the largest positive integer is $2^{31} - 1 \approx 210^9$, and the most negative integer is -2^{31} . Some machines (Cray for example) may use up to 64 bits (having 64 bit words).

Real numbers are more difficult to represent. One uses the so$-$called floating point format, which is given in the form

$$\text{real number} = 2^{\pm \text{exponent}} * (\pm \text{fraction}) . \tag{32}$$

The fraction, called "mantissa" in this context, is between 0 and 1 in magnitude and is represented by a finite number of bits. Similarly, a finite number of bits is used for the exponent. This gives us a finite dynamic range of floating$-$point numbers, essentially given by the exponent range, and finite precision. Typically we have

32$-$bit word   8 bit exponent   24 bit mantissa   accuracy $\approx 10^{-6}$
64$-$bit word   16 bit exponent   48 bit mantissa   accuracy $\approx 10^{-14}$

In some machines, the sign bit of the fraction goes into the exponent field, giving a little extra precision for a slightly reduced dynamic range.

It is quite clear, therefore, that real numbers are discrete objects within a computer: there is always a <u>finite</u> interval between two "adjacent" real numbers, the size of this interval being given by the above accuracy column. We therefore <u>cannot</u> determine any number to better than one part in 10^6 (approximately) if we use only 32$-$bit floating$-$point numbers. The only way to achieve higher precision, that is to obtain results to more significant digits than given above, is to use more bits for the representation of real numbers. This is the reason why supercomputers always have 64$-$bit words: if one does many computations, one does want to have sufficient precision to be safe against rounding errors for most algorithms. Some machines may even be used to do calculations with 128 bit representations for floating$-$point numbers, but this is very rarely necessary.

Because of this finite representation, it is clear that we may encounter situations where

$$a + b = a \quad \underline{and} \quad b \neq 0, \tag{33}$$

i.e., a number (b here) may be non–zero, but equal to zero to machine accuracy if added to some other number. Consider $a = 1$, $b = 10^{-10}$ on a 32–bit machine. Adding b to a would amount to some modification in the 34th bit of the mantissa, but the mantissa has only 24 bits ! So within machine representation, the result of the addition is no different from a itself. Another example would be $a = 10^{10}$, $b = 1$, giving the same effect and showing that b need not be small in absolute terms, but just relative to the quantity it is added to.

In the context of the bisection algorithm, halving of the interval may proceed until finally upper and lower bound differ by only a single,the least significant, bit . The root of $f(x)$ has then been determined to the highest accuracy possible with the chosen representation of real numbers. One must therefore provide some means to test for this case in implementations of the algorithm, usually in the form of testing whether $(a + b)/2 = a$ or $= b$, in which case maximum precision has been achieved. Another possible solution is to limit the number of iterations to only a little more than the number of bits in the machine word since with the interval–halving algorithm, one extra bit of precision is obtained at each iteration. One says the method converges linearly (ϵ_n is the possible error in the n–th iteration), i.e.,

$$\epsilon_{n+1} = const. * (\epsilon_n)^m \qquad \text{with} \qquad m = 1 \qquad \text{and} \qquad const. = \frac{1}{2}. \tag{34}$$

A method with $m = 2$ is said to converge quadratically, and so on.

The bisection method can be applied without any prior condition for the function $f(x)$: $f(x)$ may even be discontinuous! If we require some more stringent limitations on $f(x)$, faster convergent algorithms can be constructed, though with the drawback of being less robust in application. They may be of interest, therefore, if $f(x)$ is extremely costly to evaluate and known to be well–behaved, without the kind of problems to be discussed below.

In our discussion of differential equations we made use of Taylor's series to extrapolate the solutions. We can do the same for finding roots since when we have an abscissa close to a root and can evaluate the function as well as its first derivative, we can approximate the function by its tangent and find the root of the tangent. Since the tangent is a linear equation, this latter task is quite easy. The root of the tangent will in many cases give us an improved estimate for the root of $f(x)$, and again we can iterate this algorithm. If we indeed have an abscissa sufficiently close to the desired root of $f(x)$, the error in our estimation of the root will be small compared to the error of the original abscissa, because the error made in replacing the function $f(x)$ by its tangent is proportional to $(\Delta x)^2$. The condition is, of course, that this truncation of the Taylor series makes any sense at all. If we are far away from the root we are looking for, and a number of maxima and/or minima is located between the current abscissa and the root location, this method will essentially generate random numbers and nothing else.

Algorithm: Method of Newton–Raphson. Given an abscissa x, and the value of the function $f(x)$ as well as its first derivative $f'(x)$, estimate an improved value for a root location from

$$x_{new} = x - \frac{f(x)}{f'(x)}. \tag{35}$$

The method converges quadratically, i.e., $m = 2$ in (34), if and only if the initial estimate is sufficiently close to a root of $f(x)$. Variant: if the derivative cannot be computed rigorously, some approximation (finite differences maybe, $f'(x) = [f(x + h) - f(x)]/h$) may do; however, then the convergence may become only linear.

There is a significant danger with this algorithm when applied to very large values of x, due to the division by f', which may become small. It is therefore a good idea to <u>combine</u> this method with the previous one, so that whenever you evaluate $f(x)$, you will be able to determine a new bounding interval. It can then be ensured that (35) does not throw you out to infinity. Simply reject any new x values which fall outside the interval <u>known</u> to bound the root.

More than one dimension. Many problems in science come down to solving <u>systems</u> of non—linear equations. The method of bisection cannot be generalized to more than one dimension; you can convince yourself of that fact by considering the problem of locating a point in a plane. The Newton—Raphson method, however, <u>can</u> be generalized, including the variant. In order to solve n nonlinear equations in n unknowns, $\mathbf{f}(\mathbf{x}) = \mathbf{0}$, assuming some initial trial vector $\mathbf{x}$, a refined (vector) estimate for a solution may be obtained from

$$\mathbf{x_{new}} = \mathbf{x} - \left[\frac{\partial f_i}{\partial x_k}\right]^{-1} \mathbf{f}(\mathbf{x}), \qquad (36)$$

where $[...]^{-1}$ denotes the inverse of the $n \times n$ matrix of derivatives. Again, in many cases one does <u>not</u> need to compute the exact derivatives, but just some suitable estimate for it. In many cases, these derivatives can be obtained from the physics involved. Of course, (36) must be iterated until convergence is achieved to the desired accuracy.

Problem 3: Determination of Turning Points.

Devise a solution to the problem (posed above) of determining the classical turning points for the 6—12 potential, thogh <u>not</u> of course by employing the substitution and solution of the quadratic equation (you may do that in order to verify your results). Find both turning points for total energies $E=-.2, -.4, -.6, -.8$ reduced units, using either the bisection method <u>or</u> the Newton—Raphson method (you are not of course discouraged from using both methods!). When using the Newton—Raphson method, you <u>may or may not</u> use the interval bounding technique as you go along; but I suggest that you try it, even though the present problem should not be too difficult for Newton—Raphson to work without that safety—catch.

Write a subroutine to carry out <u>all iterations</u> of the root—finding process, to the machine's accuracy:

```
    subroutine rootf (e, rmin, rmax, r)
input : e      energy value where turning point desired ( < 0 )
        rmin   lower limit of bounding interval
        rmax   upper limit of bounding interval
output : r     location of root
```

The shellscript for compiling and executing this problem is "execroot"; you therefore type "execroot myroot" if your subroutine(s) is/are in file "myroot.f". Suggestion: have a subroutine for $f(x)$ [and $f'(x)$, if required]. Print out within f argument and value for each call!

Scaffold for problem # 3:

```
        program findr
```

```
c root finder scaffold
   1    write (*,*) 'enter energy, r_min, r_max'
        read (*,*) e,rmin,rmax
        write (*,*) 'e=',e,' r_min=',rmin,' r_max=',rmax
c
        call rootf (e,rmin,rmax,r)
c
        write (*,*) '     root at r=',r
        goto 1
        end
```

This problem does not use any graphical output. It therefore can be carried out on <u>any</u> machine whatsoever.

```
cat prob3.f
        function f(e,r)
c 6-12 potential minus energy
        r6=r**(-6)
        f=4.*(r6*r6-r6) - e
        write (*,*) e,r,f
        return
        end
        subroutine rootf (e,a,b,x)
c root finder by bisection method
        fa=f(e,a)
        fb=f(e,b)
        if (fa*fb .gt.  0.)  then
                write (*,*) 'bounding interval incorrect'
                x=0.
                return
        endif
c
c iterate interval refinement
   1    x=(a+b)/2.
        if (x .eq.  a .or.  x .eq.  b) return
        fx=f(e,x)
        if (fx .eq.  0.)  return
c which bound to replace ?
        if (fa*fx .lt.  0.)  then
                b=x
                fb=fx
        else
                a=x
                fa=fx
        endif
        goto 1
        end
jgz%
```

```
    enter energy, r_min, r_max
-.2  1  1.1
e= -0.200000   r_min=  1.000000   r_max=  1.100000
-0.200000   1.000000    0.200000
-0.200000   1.100000   -0.783373
-0.200000   1.050000   -0.557511
-0.200000   1.025000   -0.274964
-0.200000   1.012500   -6.66662e-02
-0.200000   1.006250    5.86118e-02
-0.200000   1.009375   -5.94096e-03
-0.200000   1.007813    2.58464e-02
-0.200000   1.008594    9.83115e-03
-0.200000   1.008984    1.91493e-03
-0.200000   1.009180   -2.02160e-03
-0.200000   1.009082   -5.44041e-05
-0.200000   1.009033    9.32172e-04
-0.200000   1.009058    4.38884e-04
-0.200000   1.009070    1.91167e-04
-0.200000   1.009076    6.90967e-05
-0.200000   1.009079    8.06153e-06
-0.200000   1.009081   -2.19792e-05
-0.200000   1.009080   -5.28991e-06
-0.200000   1.009079    1.86265e-06
-0.200000   1.009079   -7.59959e-07
       root at r=   1.009079
    enter energy, r_min, r_max
-.2  1.1  10
   e= -0.200000   r_min=  1.100000   r_max=  10.000000
-0.200000    1.100000   -0.783373
-0.200000   10.000000    0.199996
-0.200000    5.550000    0.199863
-0.200000    3.325000    0.197042
-0.200000    2.212500    0.166190
-0.200000    1.656250    1.56094e-02
-0.200000    1.378125   -0.298656
-0.200000    1.517187   -0.101073
-0.200000    1.586719   -3.49398e-02
-0.200000    1.621484   -7.97240e-03
-0.200000    1.638867    4.21281e-03
-0.200000    1.630176   -1.77766e-03
-0.200000    1.634521    1.24264e-03
-0.200000    1.632349   -2.61217e-04
-0.200000    1.633435    4.92170e-04
-0.200000    1.632892    1.15916e-04
-0.200000    1.632620   -7.25240e-05
-0.200000    1.632756    2.17855e-05
-0.200000    1.632688   -2.53022e-05
```

```
-0.200000    1.632722   -1.84774e-06
-0.200000    1.632739    9.86457e-06
-0.200000    1.632731    4.00841e-06
-0.200000    1.632726    1.16229e-06
-0.200000    1.632724   -4.02331e-07
-0.200000    1.632725    3.42727e-07
-0.200000    1.632725   -4.47035e-08
-0.200000    1.632725    1.34110e-07
-0.200000    1.632725    4.47035e-08
        root at r=   1.632725
     enter energy, r_min, r_max
-.4  1  1.1
     e=  -0.400000    r_min=   1.000000    r_max=   1.100000
-0.400000    1.000000    0.400000
-0.400000    1.100000   -0.583373
-0.400000    1.050000   -0.357511
-0.400000    1.025000   -7.49639e-02
-0.400000    1.012500    0.133334
-0.400000    1.018750    2.26127e-02
-0.400000    1.021875   -2.77358e-02
-0.400000    1.020312   -2.96244e-03
-0.400000    1.019531    9.72238e-03
-0.400000    1.019922    3.35589e-03
-0.400000    1.020117    1.92553e-04
-0.400000    1.020215   -1.38745e-03
-0.400000    1.020166   -5.97805e-04
-0.400000    1.020141   -2.02984e-04
-0.400000    1.020129   -4.61936e-06
-0.400000    1.020123    9.36091e-05
-0.400000    1.020126    4.54485e-05
-0.400000    1.020128    2.06530e-05
-0.400000    1.020128    6.58631e-06
-0.400000    1.020129    1.57952e-06
-0.400000    1.020129   -5.66244e-07
        root at r=   1.020129
     enter energy, r_min, r_max
-.4  1.1  10
     e=  -0.400000    r_min=   1.100000    r_max=  10.000000
-0.400000    1.100000   -0.583373
-0.400000   10.000000    0.399996
-0.400000    5.550000    0.399863
-0.400000    3.325000    0.397042
-0.400000    2.212500    0.366190
-0.400000    1.656250    0.215609
-0.400000    1.378125   -9.86556e-02
-0.400000    1.517187    9.80272e-03
-0.400000    1.447656    1.26368e-02
```

```
-0.400000    1.412891    -3.96099e-02
-0.400000    1.430273    -1.26664e-02
-0.400000    1.438965     1.85817e-04
-0.400000    1.434619    -6.18958e-03
-0.400000    1.436792    -2.98923e-03
-0.400000    1.437878    -1.39850e-03
-0.400000    1.438421    -6.05553e-04
-0.400000    1.438693    -2.09689e-04
-0.400000    1.438829    -1.18315e-05
-0.400000    1.438897     8.71718e-05
-0.400000    1.438863     3.76105e-05
-0.400000    1.438846     1.28150e-05
-0.400000    1.438837     5.96046e-07
-0.400000    1.438833    -5.51343e-06
-0.400000    1.438835    -2.44379e-06
-0.400000    1.438836    -1.01328e-06
-0.400000    1.438837    -2.98023e-07
-0.400000    1.438837     8.94070e-08
-0.400000    1.438837    -1.19209e-07
        root at r=   1.438837
    enter energy, r_min, r_max
-.6  1  1.1
    e= -0.600000   r_min=  1.000000   r_max=  1.100000
-0.600000    1.000000     0.600000
-0.600000    1.100000    -0.383373
-0.600000    1.050000    -0.157511
-0.600000    1.025000     0.125036
-0.600000    1.037500    -3.56423e-02
-0.600000    1.031250     3.93356e-02
-0.600000    1.034375     5.74470e-04
-0.600000    1.035937    -1.78443e-02
-0.600000    1.035156    -8.71432e-03
-0.600000    1.034766    -4.09019e-03
-0.600000    1.034570    -1.76251e-03
-0.600000    1.034473    -5.95212e-04
-0.600000    1.034424    -1.18017e-05
-0.600000    1.034399     2.81453e-04
-0.600000    1.034412     1.33872e-04
-0.600000    1.034418     6.11544e-05
-0.600000    1.034421     2.56300e-05
-0.600000    1.034422     7.03335e-06
-0.600000    1.034423    -2.74181e-06
-0.600000    1.034423     2.74181e-06
-0.600000    1.034423    -5.96046e-07
-0.600000    1.034423     1.07288e-06
        root at r=   1.034423
    enter energy, r_min, r_max
```

38

```
-.6  1.1  10
  e=  -0.600000   r_min=   1.100000   r_max=   10.000000
-0.600000    1.100000   -0.383373
-0.600000   10.000000    0.599996
-0.600000    5.550000    0.599863
-0.600000    3.325000    0.597042
-0.600000    2.212500    0.566190
-0.600000    1.656250    0.415609
-0.600000    1.378125    0.101344
-0.600000    1.239063   -0.199901
-0.600000    1.308594   -3.79468e-02
-0.600000    1.343359    3.51887e-02
-0.600000    1.325977   -5.40555e-04
-0.600000    1.334668    1.75400e-02
-0.600000    1.330322    8.55309e-03
-0.600000    1.328149    4.01950e-03
-0.600000    1.327063    1.74284e-03
-0.600000    1.326520    6.01947e-04
-0.600000    1.326248    3.07560e-05
-0.600000    1.326112   -2.54869e-04
-0.600000    1.326180   -1.12116e-04
-0.600000    1.326214   -4.06504e-05
-0.600000    1.326231   -4.94719e-06
-0.600000    1.326240    1.28746e-05
-0.600000    1.326236    4.11272e-06
-0.600000    1.326233   -2.38419e-07
-0.600000    1.326234    1.90735e-06
-0.600000    1.326234    5.96046e-07
-0.600000    1.326234    1.78814e-07
-0.600000    1.326234   -1.19209e-07
       root at r=   1.326234
   enter energy, r_min, r_max
-.8  1  1.1
  e=  -0.800000   r_min=   1.000000   r_max=   1.100000
-0.800000    1.000000    0.800000
-0.800000    1.100000   -0.183373
-0.800000    1.050000    4.24886e-02
-0.800000    1.075000   -0.112430
-0.800000    1.062500   -4.77961e-02
-0.800000    1.056250   -6.20383e-03
-0.800000    1.053125    1.72086e-02
-0.800000    1.054688    5.27412e-03
-0.800000    1.055469   -5.21123e-04
-0.800000    1.055078    2.36255e-03
-0.800000    1.055274    9.16541e-04
-0.800000    1.055371    1.96993e-04
-0.800000    1.055420   -1.62065e-04
```

```
-0.800000   1.055396    1.72257e-05
-0.800000   1.055408   -7.26581e-05
-0.800000   1.055402   -2.75970e-05
-0.800000   1.055399   -5.90086e-06
-0.800000   1.055397    5.54323e-06
-0.800000   1.055398   -4.17233e-07
-0.800000   1.055398    2.92063e-06
-0.800000   1.055398    1.01328e-06
-0.800000   1.055398    5.96046e-08
       root at r=   1.055398
   enter energy, r_min, r_max
-.8  1.1  2
    e=  -0.800000   r_min=   1.100000   r_max=   2.000000
-0.800000   1.100000   -0.183373
-0.800000   2.000000    0.738477
-0.800000   1.550000    0.532351
-0.800000   1.325000    0.197401
-0.800000   1.212500   -6.26691e-02
-0.800000   1.268750    7.09376e-02
-0.800000   1.240625    3.84098e-03
-0.800000   1.226563   -2.97139e-02
-0.800000   1.233594   -1.29784e-02
-0.800000   1.237110   -4.57561e-03
-0.800000   1.238867   -3.68774e-04
-0.800000   1.239746    1.73575e-03
-0.800000   1.239307    6.83367e-04
-0.800000   1.239087    1.57356e-04
-0.800000   1.238977   -1.05560e-04
-0.800000   1.239032    2.56896e-05
-0.800000   1.239005   -3.99947e-05
-0.800000   1.239018   -7.21216e-06
-0.800000   1.239025    9.00030e-06
-0.800000   1.239022    1.07288e-06
-0.800000   1.239020   -2.80142e-06
-0.800000   1.239021   -7.74860e-07
-0.800000   1.239021   0.
       root at r=   1.239021
          function f(e,r,f1)
c 6-12 potential minus energy, with derivative
          r6=r**(-6)
          f=4.*(r6*r6-r6) - e
          f1=24.*(r6-2.*r6*r6)/r
          write (*,*) e,r,f,f1
          return
          end
           subroutine rootf (e,a,b,x)
c root finder by newton-raphson method, with interval check
```

```
        fa=f(e,a,f1a)
        fb=f(e,b,f1b)
        if (fa*fb .gt.  0.)  then
                write (*,*) 'bounding interval incorrect'
                x=0.
                return
        endif
c initialize point-iterate at a
        x=(a+b)/2.
        fx=f(e,x,f1)
c
c iterate newton-raphson
    1   x=x-fx/f1
        if (x .lt.  a) then
                write (*,*) 'thrown out'
                return
        endif
        if (x .gt.  b) then
                write (*,*) 'thrown out'
                return
        endif
        if (x .eq.  a .or.  x .eq.  b) return
        fx=f(e,x,f1)
        if (fx .eq.  0.)  return
c which bound to replace ?
        if (fa*fx .lt.  0.)  then
                b=x
                fb=fx
        else
                a=x
                fa=fx
        endif
        goto 1
        end
  enter energy, r_min, r_max
-.2 1 1.1
  e=  -0.200000   r_min=  1.000000   r_max=  1.100000
-0.200000   1.000000   0.200000  -24.00000
-0.200000   1.100000  -0.783373  -1.588091
-0.200000   1.050000  -0.557511  -8.399084
  thrown out
    root at r=  0.983622
  enter energy, r_min, r_max
-.2 1 1.05
  e=  -0.200000   r_min=  1.000000   r_max=  1.050000
-0.200000   1.000000   0.200000  -24.00000
-0.200000   1.050000  -0.557511  -8.399084
```

```
-0.200000    1.025000   -0.274964  -14.62981
-0.200000    1.006205    5.95672e-02  -21.30813
-0.200000    1.009001    1.58830e-03  -20.18119
-0.200000    1.009079    1.86265e-06  -20.15021
-0.200000    1.009079   -7.59959e-07  -20.15016
      root at r=   1.009079
   enter energy, r_min, r_max
-.2 1.1 5
   e=  -0.200000   r_min=   1.100000   r_max=   5.000000
-0.200000    1.100000   -0.783373  -1.588091
-0.200000    5.000000    0.199744   3.07161e-04
-0.200000    3.050000    0.195037   9.75061e-03
   thrown out
      root at r=  -16.95256
   enter energy, r_min, r_max
-.2 1.1 4
   e=  -0.200000   r_min=   1.100000   r_max=   4.000000
-0.200000    1.100000   -0.783373  -1.588091
-0.200000    4.000000    0.199024   1.46413e-03
-0.200000    2.550000    0.185504   3.39828e-02
   thrown out
      root at r=  -2.908770
   enter energy, r_min, r_max
-.2 1.1 3
   e=  -0.200000   r_min=   1.100000   r_max=   3.000000
-0.200000    1.100000   -0.783373  -1.588091
-0.200000    3.000000    0.194521   1.09438e-02
-0.200000    2.050000    0.146833   0.153487
   thrown out
      root at r=   1.093353
   enter energy, r_min, r_max
-.2 1.1 2
   e=  -0.200000   r_min=   1.100000   r_max=   2.000000
-0.200000    1.100000   -0.783373  -1.588091
-0.200000    2.000000    0.138477   0.181641
-0.200000    1.550000   -6.76488e-02   0.955541
-0.200000    1.620796   -8.47180e-03   0.726684
-0.200000    1.632455   -1.87710e-04   0.694733
-0.200000    1.632725   -4.47035e-08   0.694009
-0.200000    1.632725    4.47035e-08   0.694009
      root at r=   1.632725
   enter energy, r_min, r_max
-.6 1 1.1
   e=  -0.600000   r_min=   1.000000   r_max=   1.100000
-0.600000    1.000000    0.600000  -24.00000
-0.600000    1.100000   -0.383373  -1.588091
-0.600000    1.050000   -0.157511  -8.399084
```

```
-0.600000   1.031247    3.93797e-02  -12.82607
-0.600000   1.034317    1.27184e-03  -12.00482
-0.600000   1.034423    1.07288e-06  -11.97720
-0.600000   1.034423   -5.96046e-07  -11.97717
      root at r=  1.034423
   enter energy, r_min, r_max
-.6 1.1 10
   e= -0.600000   r_min=  1.100000   r_max=  10.000000
-0.600000   1.100000   -0.383373  -1.588091
-0.600000  10.000000    0.599996    2.40000e-06
-0.600000   5.550000    0.599863    1.47955e-04
   thrown out
      root at r=  -4048.804
   enter energy, r_min, r_max
-.6 1.1 5
   e= -0.600000   r_min=  1.100000   r_max=   5.000000
-0.600000   1.100000   -0.383373  -1.588091
-0.600000   5.000000    0.599744    3.07161e-04
-0.600000   3.050000    0.595037    9.75061e-03
   thrown out
      root at r=  -57.97562
   enter energy, r_min, r_max
-.6 1.1 4
   e= -0.600000   r_min=  1.100000   r_max=   4.000000
-0.600000   1.100000   -0.383373  -1.588091
-0.600000   4.000000    0.599024    1.46413e-03
-0.600000   2.550000    0.585504    3.39828e-02
   thrown out
      root at r=  -14.67943
   enter energy, r_min, r_max
-.6 1.1 3
   e= -0.600000   r_min=  1.100000   r_max=   3.000000
-0.600000   1.100000   -0.383373  -1.588091
-0.600000   3.000000    0.594521    1.09438e-02
-0.600000   2.050000    0.546833    0.153487
   thrown out
      root at r=  -1.512736
   enter energy, r_min, r_max
-.6 1.1 2
   e= -0.600000   r_min=  1.100000   r_max=   2.000000
-0.600000   1.100000   -0.383373  -1.588091
-0.600000   2.000000    0.538477    0.181641
-0.600000   1.550000    0.332351    0.955541
-0.600000   1.202185   -0.286110    2.231794
-0.600000   1.330383    8.67832e-03  2.080014
-0.600000   1.326210   -4.88162e-05  2.103429
-0.600000   1.326234    1.78814e-07   2.103299
```

```
-0.600000    1.326234    -1.19209e-07    2.103300
     root at r=   1.326234
```

1.6 Statics and Dynamics of Strings

We now turn to the configuration of a string stretched between two anchoring points, subject to a tension T, shown below.

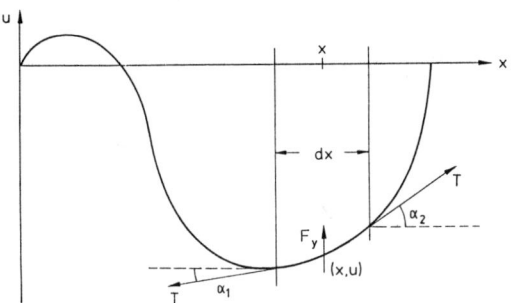

We assume that the problem is totally dominated by restoring forces due to the string tension T, and that any stiffness of the string can be neglected. This is of course totally opposed to the problem of a bar bending under stress, which is dominated by stiffness. In the latter case, tension can usually be neglected. The string is considered to be one–dimensional, i.e., the cross–section of the string is taken to be a point, and the displacements are assumed to be small (in a sense to become clear below).

Any motion of the string is described by a function $u(x,t)$ giving the displacement at position x and time t. Let us find an equation for $u(x,t)$ by considering an element dx of the string. The tension T will have different directions at the two ends of this element, resulting in a residual force acting on the element. The components of this force are

$$dF_x = T \cos \alpha_2 - T \cos \alpha_1 = O(\alpha^2) \longrightarrow 0, \tag{37}$$

and

$$dF_y = T \sin \alpha_2 - T \sin \alpha_1 = T(\tan\alpha_2 - \tan\alpha_1) + O(\alpha^2). \tag{38}$$

We will neglect forces in the x–direction, which are of order α^2 [from (37)]. Since this will introduce errors of this order, we may equally well replace the sin in (38) by tan for convenience, introducing errors of the same order. Our approximation is now clear. We retain only terms linear in the angular displacement from a straight line, therefore we will have to examine our results at the end in order to verify the validity of this assumption and to find regimes where this assumption will break down (very high frequencies or large linear displacements).

The tan is more convenient since $\tan\alpha = \partial u/\partial x$. The derivative of u vs. x at the boundaries of the interval dx can be expressed by Taylor expansion in terms of the derivative at the center:

$$dF_y = T \left[\frac{\partial u}{\partial x} + \frac{\partial}{\partial x}\left(\frac{\partial u}{\partial x}\right)\frac{dx}{2} - \frac{\partial u}{\partial x} + \frac{\partial}{\partial x}\left(\frac{\partial u}{\partial x}\right)\frac{dx}{2} \right] = T\frac{\partial^2 u}{\partial x^2}dx. \tag{39}$$

Equation (39) gives the restoring force acting on element dx at position x and time t (recall that $u = u(x,t)$).

Consider the string under a given load (e.g., a tightrope walker). The restoring forces will then balance the load so that

$$T\frac{\partial^2 u}{\partial x^2}dx = g\sigma(x)dx, \tag{40}$$

where $\sigma(x)$ is the mass density of the load per unit length, and g the gravitational constant, assuming loading due to a heavy object. The factor dx can be cancelled, of course.

In (40) we are interested in the steady state, that is $u(x,t)$ independent of t. The partial derivative is then identical to a total derivative, and we now proceed to obtain a numerical solution for the equilibrium displacements $u(x)$. One could consider the initial value methods, like Euler and Runge–Kutta, studied previously, beginning at $x = 0$ and integrating to $x = L$ (the other boundary point). However, the problem posed requires that the solution $u(x = L) = 0$ satisfies the boundary condition of no displacement at the anchoring points. Moreover, the initial condition at $x = 0$ is specified only incompletely as we need two initial conditions for a second–order equation, but have only one: $u(x = 0) = 0$. These two problems are related.

Algorithm: Shooting Method. Select an arbitrary derivative as the initial condition at $x = 0$. With the two initial conditions (derivative and $u(x = 0) = 0$) integrate out to $x = L$, resulting in as $u(L)$ that is presumably non–zero. This $u(L)$ is a (non–linear) function of the derivative chosen initially. Use a non–linear equation solver in order to find $u(L) = 0$ as function of the initial derivative.

This algorithm is rather time–consuming since at each iteration of the equation solver one has to solve the differential equation initial value problem. Furthermore, it is frequently impossible to satisfy the condition $u(L) = 0$. If we change the initial derivative by one in the least significant bit position, i.e., if we consider "adjacent real numbers", the solution at $x = L$ $u(L)$ may still vary from minus a large number to plus a large number: the initial–value problem introduces an artificial non–symmetry into the solution; $u(0)$ and $u(L)$ are treated quite differently. (Another route is to transform the differential equation into an integral equation, and then solve the integral equation. We will not discuss this approach in detail, though this _is_ sometimes useful.)

Let us try to convert the problem to an algebraic one. First we have to obtain a finite set of unknowns representing the continuous function $u(x)$. There are several ways of doing this, including finite element methods, expansion into basis functions

$$u(x) = \sum c_i\phi_i(x), \tag{41}$$

with Fourier decomposition as a special case, or finite difference methods. In the latter case we discretize space by means of some suitable mesh. The simplest discretization is an equidistant one, $x_i = i*h$, with stepsize h. We then have to express the second derivative in (40) in terms of the $u(x_i)$, the function values at the mesh points. Using "central differences", the second derivative at i can be expressed in terms of the first derivatives at $i - 1/2$ and $i + 1/2$, i.e.,

$$\left.\frac{\partial^2 u(x)}{\partial x^2}\right|_{x=x_i} = \frac{1}{h}\left(\left.\frac{\partial u}{\partial x}\right|_{x=x_{i+1/2}} - \left.\frac{\partial u}{\partial x}\right|_{x=x_{i-1/2}}\right). \tag{42}$$

The first derivatives at $i \pm 1/2$ can again be expressed as central differences, this time of function values on mesh points

$$\left.\frac{\partial u}{\partial x}\right|_{x=x_{i+1/2}} = \frac{1}{h}\left[u(x_{i+1}) - u(x_i)\right], \tag{43}$$

resulting in the final expression for the second derivative,

$$\frac{\partial^2 u(x)}{\partial x^2}\bigg|_{x=x_i} = \frac{1}{h^2}\left[u(x_{i-1}) - 2u(x_i) + u(x_{i+1})\right] + O(h^2). \tag{44}$$

In (44) the differential operator on the left hand side is approximated by the difference operator on the right hand side, accurate to terms quadratic in the stepsize h. In fact, the error is given by a constant times h^2 times the fourth derivative of u at some point within the interval considered [see H.B. Keller, Numerical Methods for Two−Point Boundary Value Problems, Blaisdell 1968]. Because of this, the solution $u(x_i)$ is also accurate up to terms of the same order.

Using (44) in (40) transforms our problem into a linear algebra problem: a linear combination of the unknowns $u(x_i) = u_i$ is equal to a given right hand side $g\sigma(x_i) = r_i$, that is, we have to solve a linear system of equations

$$
\begin{aligned}
bu_1 + au_2 &\qquad\qquad\qquad &= r_1 \\
au_1 + bu_2 + au_3 &\qquad\qquad\qquad &= r_2 \\
au - 2 + bu_3 + au_4 &\qquad\qquad\qquad &= r_3 \\
&\cdots\cdots\cdots \\
au_{n-2} + bu_{n-1} + au_n &= r_{n-1} \\
au_{n-1} + bu_n &= r_n.
\end{aligned}
\tag{45}
$$

You may ask what happened to the first term of the first difference operator, involving $u(x_0)$, and to the last term of the last difference operator, involving $u(x_{n+1})$? These displacements are the displacements at the anchoring points, and are therefore equal to zero, which is the boundary condition. The mesh has n internal points within the interval; the two boundary points do not occur explicitly since everything is known about them:

$$\bullet\ --x\ --x\ --x\ --x\ -\ \ldots\ -x\ --x\ --x\ --x\ --\bullet$$

$$0\quad 1\quad 2\quad 3\quad 4 \qquad\qquad n-3\quad n-2\quad n-1\quad n\quad n+1$$

The linear system (45) is a rather special one because the matrix is tri−diagonal and symmetric. Moreover, the diagonal elements are all equal, given by some value b, and all the off−diagonal non−zero elements are equal, given by the value a. This linear system can be solved by means of Gaussian elimination which we will derive by requiring the matrix A, (45), to be given by a product of a lower−triangular and an upper−triangular band matrix

$$A = LU, \tag{46}$$

with

$$
L = \begin{pmatrix}
\beta_1 & 0 & 0 & \cdots & & 0 \\
a_2 & \beta_2 & 0 & & & \cdot \\
0 & a_3 & \beta_3 & & & \cdot \\
\cdot & & & & & \cdot \\
\cdot & & & & & \cdot \\
0 & & \cdots & & a_n & \beta_n
\end{pmatrix}, \quad
U = \begin{pmatrix}
1 & \gamma_1 & 0 & \cdots & & 0 \\
0 & 1 & \gamma_2 & 0 & & \cdot \\
0 & 0 & 1 & \gamma_3 & 0 & \cdot \\
\cdot & & & & & \cdot \\
& & & & & \gamma_{n-1} \\
0 & \cdots & & & 0 & 1
\end{pmatrix}
$$

Carrying out the matrix multiplication $LU = A$ and requiring the matrix A to be the one given in (45), we find expressions for the β and γ:

$$a_i = a, \quad i = 1, ..., n,$$
$$\beta_1 = b, \quad \gamma_1 = \frac{a}{\beta_1},$$
$$\beta_i = b - a\gamma_{i-1}, \quad i = 2, 3, ..., n, \tag{47}$$
$$\gamma_i = \frac{a}{\beta_i}, \quad i = 2, 3, ..., n - 1.$$

Equations (47) implement the LU−decomposition of matrix A and may alternatively be derived by direct Gaussian elimination, forming linear combinations of equations successively. Having obtained the LU decomposition (46), it is straightforward to solve for the desired solution u with one intermediate step: introduce an auxilliary vector z, and solve

$$LUu = r \longrightarrow Lz = r, \qquad Uu = z \tag{48}$$

in two steps. Because the linear systems of equations (48) have triangular coefficient matrices, solution is given by the iterations

$$z_1 = \frac{r_1}{\beta_1}, \quad z_i = \frac{r_i - az_{i-1}}{\beta_i}, \quad i = 2, 3, ..., n,$$

$$\tag{49}$$

$$u_n = z_n, \quad u_i = z_i - \gamma_i u_{i+1}, \quad i = n - 1, n - 2, ..., 1.$$

With (49) we have completed the algorithm for th solution of (40). Approximate the differential operator by a suitable difference approximation, (44), decompose the resulting tri−diagonal matrix into lower and upper triangular matrices, (47), and solve the two triangular systems, (49).

The algorithm described in the previous paragraphs treats both ends of the interval as symmetrical − at least, it may seem to look like that at first sight. This is in fact not quite the case, as may be seen from the recursions in (47) and (49). Since we choose to do the elimination from top to bottom, three out of the four recursions move from left to right, and only one from right to left. (However, in practical applications this usually does not make much difference.)

We now know how to obtain a solution accurate up to order h^2 . We can vary the discretization step h in order to achieve any desired accuracy, and also achieve a solution accurate up to terms of order h^4 in a manner similar to the error estimation and improvement of the solution in the Runge−Kutta scheme. The solution on a mesh with stepsize h is improved by performing another solution with stepsize $h/2$ and extrapolating the solutions at the mesh points in common. This, however, is an immediate factor of three in the work involved. We also could get an error estimate this way, and automatically adjust the stepsize h, though of course, with decreased stepseize h we would have to redo the whole calculation, not just some last step as in the initial− value problems.

The above method of solution is much more general than actually applied here. One may use this scheme to solve <u>any</u> linear differential equation, to <u>any</u> order and for each differential operator, one can devise finite−difference representations, irrespective of order of differentiation and of order of accuracy. Naturally, higher orders will lead to more complicated difference expressions, involving more and more neighbours of the central point considered. This will lead to more than three diagonals in the matrix that are non–zero. However, there do exist efficient solvers for band matrices that are more general than tridiagonal. The tridiagonal structure remains valid for <u>arbitrary</u> linear differential equations of second order, i.e., with the occurance of first derivatives the function itself will not change the general picture, only the diagonals a and b just become functions of position instead of constants.

Problem No. 4: Tightrope Sitter.

Consider a tightrope stretched between two anchoring points 10 m apart, subject to a tension $T=1000$ kg m/sec^2 . A man is sitting on the tightrope, to be approximated by a mass distribution

$$m(x) = m_0 exp^{-(x-p)**2} \quad \text{with} \quad m_0 = 80 \text{ kg/m, and position p=10/3 m.}$$

What is the total mass of the man ? Assume the gravitational constant $g = 10$ m/sec^2 . Find the displacement of the tightrope ! Is the maximum displacement at the point of maximum load ? Why ? Write a subroutine to solve the two–point boundary value problem:

>   subroutine string (n,h,T, rm, u)
>   dimension rm(n), u(n)

Input
>   n   number of mesh points within interior region
>   h   stepsize $x_i =i*h$, boundary at x=0 and $(i+1)*h$
>   T   string tension
>   rm(1...n) mass distribution

Output
>   u(1...n) displacements at mesh points

Provided Scaffold

```
             program strmain
c string problem main program
             parameter (m=500, m1=m+1)
             dimension rm(m),u(m),xx(0:m1),pp(2),yp(2)
         *,udisp(0,m1),rmdisp(m)
c
             xl=10.
         1   write (*,*) 'enter n, # of interior pts'
             read (*,*) n
             if (n .le.  1 .or.  n .gt.  m) then
                    write (*,*) '1 < n <', m+1
                    goto 1
             endif
             h=xl/(n+1.)
             write (*,*) 'enter string tension T'
             read(*,*) T
```

```
          write (*,*) 'enter sitter mass factor m0'
          read (*,*) am0
          write (*,*) 'enter sitter position p'
          read (*,*) p
c
          do 5 i=1,n
          x=i*h
          xx(i)=x
          rmdisp(i)=exp(-(x-p)**2)
        5 rm(i)=am0*rmdisp(i)
          xx(0)=0.
          xx(n+1)=xl
c
          call string (n, h, T, rm, u)
c
c this is your subroutine
c
          do 33 i=1,n
       33 udisp(i)=u(i)
          udisp(0)=0.
          udisp(n+1)=0.
          call plotfu (xx(0),udisp(0),n+2,1,1,-.5.10.5,-9.5,1.5)
          pp(1)=p
          pp(2)=p
          yp(1)=-9.5
          yp(2)=1.5
          call plotfu (pp,yp,2,1,1,-.5,10.5,-9.5,1.5)
          call plotfu(xx(1),rmdisp,n,1,1,0,0,0,0)
c
          goto 1
          end
```

Solution for problem number 4

```
          subroutine string (n,h,T,rm,u)
          parameter (m=500)
          dimension bet(m),gam(m),r(m),z(m),u(m),rm(m)
c
c make matrix
          hh=h*h
          a=T/hh
          b=-2.*T/hh
c a is off-diagonal, b is diagonal matrix element
c
c factorize matrix
          gamold=0.
          do 2 i=1,n
          bet(i)=b-a*gamold
```

```
        gam(i)=a/bet(i)
   2    gamold= gam(i)
c
c make r.h.s.
        g=10.
        totm=0.
        do 3 i=1,n
        r(i)=g*rm(i)
   3    totm=totm+rm(i)
        write (*,*) 'totm=',totm*h
c
c solve linear systems
        zold=0.
        do 4 i=1,n
        z(i)=(r(i)-a*zold)/bet(i)
   4    zold=z(i)
        uold=0.
        do 5 i=1,n, -1
        u(i)=z(i)-gam(i)*uold
   5    uold=u(i)
        return
        end

    enter n, # of interiors pts      201
    enter string tension T           10000
    enter sitter mass factor m0      80
    enter sitter position p             3.333333
    totm=        141.7961
    u_min =    -2.786371   at   x=  3.613861
```

1.7 Dynamics of Strings

In the last section we balanced the restoring forces due to string tension by static (gravitational) load forces. Let us now consider the motion of a string in time. Assuming some initial displacement $u(x, t = 0)$, what is the configuration $u(x, t)$ of the string at time t? The time evolution of the motion for string element dx is given by application of Newton's law, $F = ma$, applied to the infinitesimal mass dm of string element dx:

$$dF_y = dm \frac{\partial^2 u}{\partial t^2}. \tag{50}$$

The mass element dm is given by the mass density $\rho(x)$ and size of the element, dx:

$$dm = \rho(x)dx. \tag{51}$$

Here we assume the linear mass density of the string to vary with position, $\rho = \rho(x)$. This density is not to be confused with the loading mass density $\sigma(x)$ defined in the previous lecture. Of course, in both cases, the masses entering the problem are the <u>sum</u> of internal string mass plus any loading masses. In the case of static load, however, we neglected the string mass with respect to the load mass. In string vibration problems, there is usually no external load mass applied to the string. In principle, to be rigorous, both mass densities σ and ρ are identical and equal to the sum of string and load mass.

The equation of motion for the vibrating string is given by once again equating the restoring force to the accelerating force, i.e.,

$$\rho(x)dx\frac{\partial^2 u}{\partial t^2} = T\frac{\partial^2 u}{\partial x^2}dx, \tag{52}$$

so that dx cancels out. This is the wave equation known from many other problems in physics. Of course, (52) is slightly unrealistic in that we have not put in any damping term; hence (52) describes undamped vibration of a string, i.e., the vibration, once started, will never cease.

There exist again a variety of methods to treat (52), and we will here consider a decomposition into eigenmodes. Since we know that the oscillation of each point of the string will be undamped, let us try an ansatz for the function $u(x, t)$. We will assume that there exists a set of frequencies ω — the eigenfrequencies of the string — and that the solution u(x,t) can be written as a superposition of some corresponding eigenfunctions. The coefficients of this superposition will depend upon time and express the variation of the motion in time.

Mathematically, this must be a valid approach since the operator $\partial^2/\partial x^2$ is a hermitean operator. It therefore has a complete orthonormal system of eigenfunctions, and it is nothing but a change of representation to transform from $u(x, t)$ to $u(\omega, t)$:

$$u(x, t) = \sum_\omega u_\omega(x)u(\omega, t). \tag{53}$$

In (53) $u_\omega(x)$ is the eigenfunction for frequency ω. Since we know that the vibration is to be periodic in time, it is reasonable to expect that the time–dependent coefficients $u(\omega, t)$ will be sin and cos; let us try out if an ansatz like that can work. We assume that the solution $u(x, t)$ can be written as

$$u(x, t) = \sum_\omega u_\omega(x)(a_\omega \sin \omega t + b_\omega \cos \omega t) \tag{54}$$

and try out this ansatz in (52). In order to do that, we have to differentiate (54), giving

$$\frac{\partial^2 u}{\partial t^2} = \sum_\omega u_\omega(x)(-\omega^2)(a_\omega \sin \omega t + b_\omega \cos \omega t), \tag{55}$$

which is rather trivial since sin and cos are differentiated easily, and $u_\omega(x)$ does not have any time dependence. Using (55) in (52) yields

$$\sum_\omega \rho(x)u_\omega(x)(-\omega^2)(a_\omega \sin \omega t + b_\omega \cos \omega t) = \sum_\omega T\frac{\partial^2 u_\omega(x)}{\partial x^2}(a_\omega \sin \omega t + b_\omega \cos \omega t). \tag{56}$$

Since (56) is valid for all x and t, we can choose to multiply this equation with some function like $\sin \omega t$ and integrate over all t. That will project out the corresponding frequency component from the sum $\sum_\omega$, so that (56) must be valid for each frequency component separately:

$$\rho(x)u_\omega(x)(-\omega^2) = T\frac{\partial^2 u_\omega(x)}{\partial x^2}. \tag{57}$$

Equation (57) simply expresses the — expected — fact that $u_\omega(x)$ must be an eigenfunction of $\partial^2/\partial x^2$. This can be seen more clearly by multiplying (57) by $-1/\rho(x)$, leading to

$$\left[-\frac{1}{\rho(x)}T\frac{\partial^2}{\partial x^2}\right]u_\omega(x) = \omega^2 u_\omega(x). \tag{58}$$

In (58) we have managed to transform the original partial differential equation in two variables (x, t), (52), into an eigenvalue problem for an ordinary differential equation; in (58) there only occurs one variable x and the partial derivative becomes identical to the total derivative. Of course, the method used implicitly here is the method of separation of variables, in that we have separated the spatial and time dependence into two factors in the solution. This method is rather general and can be applied in a large number of cases. The boundary condition, $u(x = 0, t) = 0$ and $u(x = L, t) = 0$ is implemented by requiring the boundary conditions $u_\omega(x = 0) = 0$ and $u - \omega(x = L) = 0$ for all solutions to the eigenvalue problem, (58).

The last piece missing in our solution of (52) is the treatment of initial conditions. At time $t = 0$, each element dx of the string may have a prescribed displacement $u(x, t = 0)$ and a prescribed velocity $\partial u/\partial t$. It must be possible to recover these from our general solution (54):

$$u(x, t = 0) = \sum_\omega u_\omega(x)b_\omega,$$

$$\tag{59}$$

$$\left.\frac{\partial u}{\partial t}\right|_{t=0} = \sum_\omega u_\omega(x)\omega a_\omega.$$

We may now obtain the as-yet undetermined coefficients a_ω and b_ω, which have to be chosen such that the initial conditions (59) are fulfilled. Since we know that the $u_\omega(x)$ are a complete orthonormal system of functions, we can simply integrate (59) with one specific $u_\omega(x)$ in order to project out all other terms in the sum, and obtain

$$b_\omega = \int u(x, t = 0)u_\omega(x)dx,$$

$$\tag{70}$$

$$a_\omega = \frac{1}{\omega}\int \left[\left.\frac{\partial u}{\partial t}\right|_{t=0}\right]u_\omega(x)dx.$$

Here (70) requires that the solutions $u_\omega(x)$ have been normalized to one, i.e.,

$$\int u_\omega(x)^2\,dx = 1. \tag{71}$$

The normalization of the eigenfunctions from (58) is arbitrary since (58) is a homogeneous equation and any factor would cancel out. The normalization (71) is simply the most convenient.

The only task left is now the numerical solution of (58), which is rather similar to (40) apart from the additional factor $-1/\rho(x)$ and the eigenvalue problem for homogeneous (58) [as opposed to the inhomogeneous problem (40)]. However, the central idea used to obtain a numerical algorithm for (40) is still valid. We can discretize the desired solution on some suitable mesh and transform the differential equation into an algebraic equation. Exactly the same can be done with (58), and we arrive at an eigenvalue problem for a tridiagonal matrix. Unfortunately, because of the factor $1/\rho(x)$, this matrix is <u>not</u> symmetric but given by

$$
\begin{array}{ccccc}
2T/h^2\rho_1 & -T/h^2\rho_1 & 0 & \cdots \\[2mm]
-T/h^2\rho_2 & 2T/h^2\rho_2 & -T/h^2\rho_2 & 0 & \cdots \\[2mm]
0 & -T/h^2\rho_3 & 2T/h^2\rho_3 & -T/h^2\rho_3 & 0 & \cdots \\[2mm]
\multicolumn{5}{c}{\cdots\cdots}
\end{array}
\tag{72}
$$

Using matrix notation for the finite difference operator,

$$
M = -T\frac{\partial^2}{\partial x^2}, \tag{73}
$$

where M is the symmetric matrix from the previous lecture (apart from the minus sign), (58) may be written as

$$
\frac{1}{\rho}Mu = \omega^2 u. \tag{74}
$$

We may multiply this equation by $\rho^{1/2}$ to get

$$
\rho^{-1/2}M\rho^{-1/2}(\rho^{1/2}u) = \omega^2(\rho^{1/2}u). \tag{75}
$$

It is seen that by means of this transformation we obtain a <u>symmetric</u> matrix, which is highly desirable since the eigenvalue/eigenvector problem is computationally much easier and very good algorithms exist to solve <u>symmetric</u> problems. For non−symmetric real matrices, we would have to face the problem that eigenvalues as well as eigenvectors could become complex. The above analysis shows that for the present case that cannot occur; however, any numerical routine used to do the eigenvalue/eigenvector calculation for non−symmetric matrices could not know about this, and therefore numerical errors might produce non−real results. Apart from this, diagonalization of a real tridiagonal <u>symmetric</u> matrix requires much less work. Let us summarize the steps for solution of the string vibration problem:

1. Given the geometry, i.e., L, T, and $\rho(x)$, select a discretization in terms of n meshpoints, stepsize h;

2. Set up the symmetric tridiagonal matrix $\rho^{-1/2}M\rho^{1/2}$ from (75);

3. Diagonalize this matrix to find n eigenvalues ω and corresponding eigenvectors $\rho^{1/2}u_\omega(x_i)$. This task may be solved by means of a variety of routines. Some are discussed in the "Numerical Recipes" book cited in the organizational material. Another useful reference is the EISPACK[7] program library available at almost every installation.

4. Normalize the eigenfunctions u according to (71), after division by $\rho^{1/2}(x_i)$;

5. Evaluate the integrals (70) in order to obtain a and b coefficients from the given initial conditions;

6. The complete solution is given by (54).

We do not discuss the actual numerical implementation of the eigensystem calculation partly due to a lack of space, but also because of the high quality of the EISPACK routines available. In view of the existence of, and easy access to, these routines, in most cases it is not worthwhile to consider writing one's own routines for such tasks. The same is true of solutions of linear systems of algebraic equations, where a similar package exists (LINPACK).

Final remark: The method of solution chosen for the present problem (solving the wave equation) was deliberately tailored to closely parallel the solution of problems in quantum mechanics. The Schrödinger equation may be treated by rather similar methods, and all the various techniques and manipulations employed here are common to calculations on quantum–mechanical systems.

1.8 Literature

1. FORTRAN 77 programming language: any of a very large number of books will do.

2. UNIX operating system: Mark G. Pobell, A Practical Guide to UNIX System V. Any other book on Unix will do as well.

3. Handbooks and Manuals coming with your computer, in particular Users Guides and Language Reference Manuals.

4. Computational methods: W.H. Press, B.P. Flannery, S.A. Teukolsky, W.T. Vetterling: Numerical Recipes – The Art of Scientific Computing. Recommended! Contains many further references.

5. Numerical mathematics in general: J. Stoer, R. Bulirsch, Introduction to Numerical Analysis, New York, Springer, 1980; A. Ralston, P. Rabinowitz, A First Course in Numerical Analysis, New York, McGraw–Hill, 1978.

6. C.W. Gear, Numerical Initial Value Problems in Ordinary Differential Equations, Englewood Cliffs, NJ, Prentice–Hall.

7. B.T. Smith et al., Matrix Eigensystem Routines – EISPACK Guide, 2nd ed., vol. 6 of Lecture Notes in Computer Science, New York, Springer 1976.

2. Monte Carlo Simulations in Statistical Physics

D.Stauffer, Institut for Theoretical Physics, Cologne University, 5000 Köln 41, West Germany

2.1 Introduction

In Statistical Physics one mostly deals with thermal motion of a system of particles at nonzero temperatures. For example, in a classical ideal gas of point–like molecules each particle has an average kinetic energy equal to $dk_BT/2$ in d dimensions. Here T is the absolute temperature and $k_B = 1.6 \times 10^{23}$ Joule per Kelvin is Boltzmann's constant. Statistical Physics is used try to explain such laws and to predict the properties of materials consisting of many such particles; therefore, in this example the specific heat is $3Nk_B/2$ in three dimensions if the gas consists of N particles. In most applications, the number N of particles is very large, and they influence each other by their intermolecular forces. For example, a glass of beer contains about 10^{25} water molecules, and if these molecules did not interact with each other, the beer would vanish by evaporation, not by drinking. These interactions are also unhealthy for theoretical physics since with interactions usually one cannot solve exactly the problem of how the molecules move and what their average energy is, because even on a computer it is not possible to store the positions and velocities of 10^{25} point–like molecules. (The Cray–2 supercomputer has only two Gigabytes of main memory.) Instead, one is forced to work with a much smaller number of molecules, below 10^6, and solve numerically the equations of motion arising from Newton's law: force equals mass times acceleration. This method is called *molecular dynamics* and has already been used in the first chapter of this book by Zabolitzky. We will not deal with this technique here; readers who want to know more are referred to the book of D.W.Heermann [1].

Instead Statistical Physics mostly uses a *probabilistic* (or stochastic) method: The system of interacting particles has a fluctuating energy E, because we assume that it is in contact with a heat bath. For example, some people like to study glasses of whisky cooled by ice cubes in contact with the liquid. Energy is transferred more or less randomly from the heat bath (the ice cubes) to the system of interest (the whisky), and back. Statistical Physics assumes, in agreement with more detailed theories and with experiment, that the observed equilibrium system reaches a given total energy E with a probability

$$P(E) \sim \exp(-E/k_BT),$$

where $\exp(x) = e^x$ is the exponential function. Thus we shuffle the particles around randomly according to this probability, not to Newton's law. For large enough systems, the results are usually the same. Experts call this second method an example of the *canonical ensemble* and the first method, simulated by molecular dynamics, an example of the *microcanonical ensemble*. They also like the word *Hamiltonian* instead of *energy*. (Most quantum effects are neglected in these lectures.)

In this chapter I want to avoid such names and instead simulate this probabilistic method on the computer. We tell the computer to do a certain operation with probability p by calculating a random number z which lies somewhere between zero and unity. All real numbers in that interval have the same chance to agree with that random number z. Then the given operation is executed if and only if the random number z is smaller than the probability p. For example, if $p = 0.1$ and if we produce a million different random numbers z, then about 90 % of these random numbers will be between 0.1 and 1, and only 10 % will be between 0 and 0.1. Thus the condition $z < p$ is fulfilled with probability p (the next chapter deals with the production of random numbers on a computer). If the reader has the time and the money and does not demand too much accuracy, he may also produce them on the roulette tables of the Mediterranean resort town of Monte Carlo. This more traditional method has given the probabilistic Monte Carlo simulation of $\exp(-E/k_BT)$ its name.

Still, if we had to store and to change three coordinates and three velocity components for each particle of a three–dimensional experiment, we would need a lot of computer time and memory just as for molecular dynamics methods. Simulations are much simpler if we assume that the particles can only sit on the sites of a big lattice; then each lattice site is in one of only two states: Occupied or empty. This simplification is ideal for computers; only one bit is needed for each site. Moreover, we usually assume that only nearest neighbors influence each other; thus on a simple cubic lattice each site feels the forces from only six neighboring sites. This model for fluids is called the lattice gas or (spin 1/2) Ising model.

The above formula $\exp(-E/k_BT)$ is only valid in thermal equilibrium, i.e. when the temperature of the sample is the same as that of the surrounding heat bath and when properties like the average energy no longer change with time. In recent years many growth processes and disordered systems have also been studied which are not in thermal equilibrium. The probability to occupy a site is then defined differently, and various different growth processes are possible. Related models are the so–called *cellular automata*. Of course, all these Monte Carlo methods for lattice models are much easier for the computer than the molecular dynamics for a fluid. Therefore the simulation of more than 10^{10} sites was achieved in 1986, with up to 4200 sites treated per microsecond. (The million sites barrier was broken in 1981.) But we will still have to wait before computers beat nature with its 10^{25} molecules in a glass of beer.

Common to all these models on lattices is a simple computing trick to save computing time: Use arrays with one index, not with two or three in 2 and 3 dimensions. For example, if the variables IS store the occupation status of the sites (IS=0 or $= -1$ for empty, IS=1 for occupied) in a simple cubic lattice of L*L*L sites, then it is not practical to store the sites as IS(I,J,K) with indices from 1 to L. Instead I prefer to store them as a one–dimensional array IS(K) with K from 1 to L^3. The left neighbor of site K has the index K–1, the right neighbor is K+1, the neighbor in front (in the back) is K–L (K+L), and the neighbors above and below have the index K–L*L and K+L*L. (To ensure that the sites in the top–most plane also have an upper neighbor, and the sites in the lowest plane have a lower neighbor, I often store the content of the lowest plane again in a buffer plane on top of the top–most physical plane. Similarly, the content of the highest physical plane is stored in an additional buffer plane below the lowest physical plane. Then the upper buffer has indices K from 1 to L^2, the physical sites are numbered from L^2+1 to L^3+L^2, and the lower buffer plane has sites from K=L^3+L^2+1 to K=L^3+2L^2 which agree with sites IS(L^2+1) to IS($2L^2$).) For two dimensions, a small 3*3 lattice is then stored as

$$7\ 8\ 9$$
$$1\ 2\ 3$$
$$4\ 5\ 6$$
$$7\ 8\ 9$$
$$1\ 2\ 3$$

with *italic* numbers for the buffer lines.

This method automatically leads to the so–called periodic (more precisely: helical) boundary conditions where there are no surface sites and where thus a limited number of lattice sites in general simulates better the infinitely large material than a system with free surfaces. Computer time is saved because the computer no longer has to evaluate I+J*L+K*L^2 for memory element IS(I,J,K) and because one does not need six IF–statements for the boundary sites. Moreover, on vector–computers a loop over all IS(K) (without buffers) now has L^3 elements whereas with IS(I,J,K) the loop over K has only L elements. Vector computers often do not work efficiently if the innermost loop has only a small number of elements, and L^3 is larger and thus more efficient to deal with than L.

This chapter deals first with the lattice gas in thermal equilibrium, and then with other models like cellular automata and growth processes. We end with the Kauffman model for genetics, which was invented by a physician, not a physicist. Apart from the next section on random number generation it should not be necessary to read any of the previous sections to understand the following ones. Thus the biologically inclined reader may concentrate on Eden and Kauffman models, the solid state physicist on the Ising model. An appendix gives advice on vector computing for experts. For all models, however, our emphasis will be on fast Fortran simulation of large systems, not on elegant programming or beautiful graphics display. We let the computer work for us, and not oblige us to follow its special wishes.

2.2 Random Numbers

How do we produce random numbers z distributed evenly between zero and unity ? We may call a built–in random number generator, but then we still do not know how it works. Also, the frequent call of such a subroutine usually costs a lot of computer time, and the results may not be as random as we wish. So we discuss here how to write a simple random number generator into the Fortran program.

How large is 12345 times 65539 ? It is easily estimated to be slightly below 10^9 and also is clearly an odd integer, but to know the precise result requires a tedious multiplication giving 809078955, a seemingly random sequence of digits. So this is a way to produce random numbers: We multiply large numbers and omit the leading digits. For example, if we restrict ourselves to five–digit integers, we omit the leading four digits of the product and get 78955 as our new "random" integer. Multiplying again, 78955 by 65539, and keeping only the last five digits gives another random integer, and so on and on and on...

Of course, in the interior of a computer there are no slaves multiplying with *ten* fingers; instead a computer employs electronic circuits with *two* states. Thus numbers are represented in a binary system with the digits 0 and 1, also called bits. A typical computer uses 32 bits (4 bytes) for one number. Thus random numbers can be produced by multiplying two large 32–bit numbers and keeping only the last (least significant) 32 bits. Many computers automatically omit in a multiplication all leading bits exceeding the 32–bit limit, and then

$$IBM = IBM * 65539$$

produces a new random integer IBM out of the previous random number IBM. The first value of IBM at the start of the calculation, the *seed*, is supplied by the user and must be an odd integer to avoid very short periods; the computer then produces with this algorithm all the other random integers IBM which the program requires.

However, there is a problem: The first (leftmost, most significant) bit of the 32 bits usually contains the sign, and thus the computer usually gives about half of the random integers as negative. If you do not believe that multiplication of two positive integers gives a negative integer, just try it. Of course, negative numbers also can be used provided we normalize the probabilities p correctly; thus one should avoid writing another program line which forces it to be positive. If, however, the computer does not handle the negative integers properly, one can force them to be positive with the statements

```
IBM=IBM*65539
IF(IBM.LT.0) IBM=IBM+2147483647+1
```

instead of the single multiplication above. The large integer is merely $2^{31}-1$, but since 2147483648 is too large an integer to handle on 32–bit computers, we are tricking, with our two additions, the computer into believing that we are not adding 2^{31} but a smaller number which the computer accepts. In this way one finds random odd integers between 1 and 2147483647 if one forces them to be positive, and random odd integers between -2147483647 and $+2147483647$ if, more efficiently, one also allows negative IBM and thus omits the IF–statement.

```
      IBM=12345
      DO 1 K=1,20
      IBM=IBM*65539
C     IF(IBM.LT.0) IBM=IBM+2147483647+1
1     PRINT *, IBM
      STOP
      END
```

How does one now let the computer perform a command with probability $p < 1$? Obviously the condition is no longer IF(IBM.LT.P) ..., since the random number IBM never lies between zero and unity. We can divide IBM by 2147483648.0 and then compare this ratio with p. That is inefficient for two reasons: A division often costs much more time than multiplication; thus multiply IBM with $0.465661 \ 10^{-9}$ instead. More importantly, in most applications p will be the same for millions of lattice sites, and therefore it is better to multiply p once by 2^{31} than to multiply IBM repeatedly for millions of sites by 2^{-31}. Thus with random integers IBM forced to be positive, one defines once, at the beginning of the calculation, the integer probability $2^{31}p$, or IP= P*2147483648.0. Then the condition for performing a command with probability p is simply IF(IBM.LT.IP).... If IBM can be both positive and negative we normalize p by 2^{32} instead: IP=$(2*p-1)*2147483648.0$ once before the loop starts. Within that loop we thus only need

```
      IBM=IBM*65539
      IF(IBM.LT.IP) ...
```

where the three dots stand for the command.

Of course, these random numbers are not truely random. If we repeat the calculation with the *same* seed for IBM, we will get exactly the *same* sequence of random numbers. This would not be true if the random numbers were generated, e.g., by electronic noise (cryptographers may need such irreproducible random numbers and for them suitable chips are available commercially). For us, it is very useful that we get exactly the same random numbers from the same seed. For example, we may have an idea how to speed up a running program without changing the results. Starting with the same seed and using random numbers in the same sequence, we thus should get exactly the same result; if not, we have made an error somewhere or at least do not understand the program flow completely.

On a 16–bit computer one cannot use 65539 as multiplicator; instead 899 seems to work. On computers with more than 32 bits one may find in the manual information about the multiplicator. In general it is useful to play around on the computer until one has found a way to get random numbers; in this way one learns also something about the inner workings of the computer. If the computer produces nice numbers but they repeat themselves after a short cycle, check if your random number is still odd, and not even. Are these random numbers "good", i.e. truely random and not correlated ? They are not. There are better ways, but none of them is perfect. Replacing 65539 by 16807 may be better and at least gives an alternative. Some built–in random number generators first multiply the random number and then add something to the product. Perhaps the best method is the Tausworth shift generator, which many physicists, including this author, call the Kirkpatrick–Stoll [2] method. We explain it now for readers requiring a more advanced technique; we recommend it whenever problems occur with simpler ones.

This Kirkpatrick–Stoll random number generator starts with an array of 250 random integers IR(1), IR(2), ..., IR(250). Then the next random number IR is

$$IR(251) = IR(1).XOR.IR(148)$$

where XOR is the bit–by–bit exclusive–or which is true (bit=1) if one – and only one– of its two arguments is true. One can test this function by calculating 5.XOR.6 which should give the result "3". Some computers prefer XOR(5,6), IEOR(5,6), or require special options in the compiler control statement. Again I suggest having a try and not to rely only on manuals. If your computer really refuses this bit–by–bit exclusive or, then try "–" (minus) instead, which may even be better.

Having produced in this way random number IR(251), we get IR(252) by XOR–ing or subtracting IR(2) and IR(149), etc. Generally,

$$IR(K) = IR(K-250).XOR.IR(K-103)$$

expands our array IR of random integers. To save memory we may require k to be smaller than, say, 10000; if k=10000, we shift the integers IR(9750) – IR(9999) into the memory elements IR(1) – IR(250), set k=251, and start again. An alternative is to use "periodic boundary conditions" for k, k–250 and k–103: by subtracting 250 we force them all to be positive and not larger than 250. Experts instead force these three indices to vary between 0 and 255 by making a logical bit–by–bit AND with the number 255, which is 11111111 in binary representation. (The computer then has to understand IR(0); otherwise add 1 to each index.)

How do we get the 250 initial random integers ? We could simply use the random integers obtained via IBM*65539, but then presumably the results will be not as random as desired. It is better to produce these initial values bit by bit. Thus we multiply our random integer IBM by 16807 or 65539; if it is negative we set the last bit=1 in our random number IR, whereas for positive IBM the bit stays zero. Then we shift IR by one bit to the left (multiplication by 2). After 32 such additions of unity or zero and 32 shifts to the left the random number IR contains a sequence of random bits which are 0 or 1 with equal probability. (If we use only positive random numbers, we set the bit if IBM is less than 1073741824, and never set the left–most or sign bit of the integer IR.) After the initialization is completed one should produce several hundred random numbers IR for the "waste basket" before using them in a simulation analogous to a car motor, which has to warm up first.

Leaving now the complications of Kirkpatrick–Stoll methods, we ask how we can find out if a random number generator is good. It will not be very helpful to the user if he knows that the generator passed or failed a mathematical test with little connection to the physics problem to be simulated. Instead you may try to fill up a cube of L*L*L sites: A site is selected randomly, and it is filled (=1) if it was empty (=0) whereas it is left untouched if it was already filled. If you get the x–coordinate of the site to be checked by one random number (and suitable normalization to give an index between 1 and L), then the y–coordinate from another random number and finally the z–coordinate from a third consecutive random number, then you may check if the fraction of empty sites decays to zero exponentially. With the simple 65539 rule it fails drastically to do so, even for L = 20. The problem vanishes, however, if we store all sites as a one–dimensional array with one index instead of three. Thus the difficulties are produced by triplet correlations between consecutive random numbers.

More sophisticated is another test (which I learned from Naeem Jan and David Mac-Donald) for correlations between two strings of random numbers IBM1=IBM1*65539 and IBM2=IBM2*65539. Let us start IBM1 with an initial value ISEED and IBM2 with ISEED+2, and then produce 100 pairs of random numbers IBM1(K) and IBM2(K). We find for which of these k–values (k=1,2,..100) the two numbers IBM1(K) and IBM2(K) agree to within 5 % of the total interval available for random numbers, obtaining approximately 10 of them, distributed about randomly between 1 and 100. Everything seems fine until we repeat the experiment with a different ISEED (equal, say, to the last known value of IBM1). Then we will find in all or most cases that agreement to within 5 % occurs at exactly the same value as before, which should not be the case for random numbers. Repeating the experiment a third, or a thousandth time only confirms the problem; separating the initial seeds by a number larger than 2 does not solve it. However, if we use 65539 for IBM1 and 16807 for IBM2 then these unwanted correlations vanish (thus indicating that the program was written correctly.) Even the Kirkpatrick–Stoll random number generator shows slight correlations in this aspect if we fail to warm it up.

Pointing out problems is useful, but what about solutions? I suggest making some simulations with a different (slower) type of random number generator. If the results do not change, within statistical accuracy, then one may have good random numbers. (The less bits the computer word has, the more problematic are its random numbers and the more cautious one should be.) In this way one tests the quality in relation to the specific problem being dealt with. However, in most cases the systematic errors due to the extrapolations needed in statistical physics will be larger than the purely statistical errors, and these will be larger than the errors from bad random numbers; and all that assumes that the program had no errors! Thus there are many reasons why computer simulators should not claim to be absolutely sure of anything.

EXERCISE: Write a program which occupies each site of a 30*30 lattice randomly with probability p.

2.3 Ising Model

More than 60 years ago Prof.Lenz suggested to his graduate student Ernst Ising a problem which, after a long time lag, challenged numerous later scientists and is still not exactly solved in three dimensions. Ising himself, a German Jew, survived Nazism but did not profit much from the Ising model (lattice gas) which we have already defined qualitatively in the Introduction; how does it look like precisely and how does one program its Monte Carlo simulation ?

Each lattice site i has two states; it is either occupied, $S_k = 1$, or empty, $S_k = -1$. Each site tends to force its nearest lattice neighbors into the same state it has itself. In addition, an external force B acting identically on all sites may favor the value $+1$ over the value -1. Quantitatively this is expressed through the energy

$$E = -J \sum_{i<k} \sum S_i S_k - B \sum_k S_k,$$

where the double sum $(i < k)$ runs over all pairs of nearest neighbors, and the simple sum over all sites. Following widespread usage we call S_k the spin, J the exchange energy and B (often denoted by H) the magnetic field. In most research on this Ising model, as well as in these lectures, the quantum mechanical aspects of atomic spins are neglected apart from the fact that S_k can only take the values ± 1. Readers afraid of magnetism may instead think of a fluid with occupation variables $n_k = (1 + S_k)/2$ which are zero for an empty site and unity for an occupied site. Then an "up" spin corresponds to a molecule at that site, and a "down" spin to a vacuum; $2B$ is the chemical potential (apart from an additive constant). Alternatively one may think of political choices in a two–party system, where neighbors try to talk each other into voting for the Right or Left. (Speculations that this author never votes for a small party are unproven; quantum mechanics does also allow for more complicated spins like $S_k = 1$, 0 and -1, only computers run better on one–bit variables.) If we look at one particular pair, i and k, of nearest neighbors, they contribute $-JS_iS_k$ to the double sum in the energy. If these two spins are parallel, this contribution is $-J$, and if they are antiparallel it is $+J$. Thus

2J is the energy to break a bond between neighbors,

be that bond magnetic or political. In the elements iron, cobalt and nickel such magnetic bonds lead to ferromagnetism (below the critical temperature T_c), which means that even without a magnetic field B nearly all spins S_k within a magnetic domain are parallel (have the same sign). The difference between the number of up and down spins, i.e. the sum $\sum_k S_k$, is called the magnetization; normalized by the number of spins in the lattice we denote it by M, with $-1 < M < 1$.

Monte Carlo studies of these and numerous similar models use the following technique to simulate the thermal probabilities $\exp(-E/k_BT)$ discussed in the Introduction:

1: Select a spin S_k to be investigated.
2: Calculate the energy change $\Delta E = E_{new} - E_{old}$ associated with a possible spin flip of S_k into $-S_k$.
3: Compare a random number z, with $0 < z < 1$, with the thermal probability $p = \exp(-\Delta E/k_BT)$ to flip that spin.
4: Flip spin, $S_k = -S_k$, if and only if $z < p$.
5: Use present configuration, whether S_k was flipped or not, to calculate any desired averages.

We repeat these five commands over and over again. If we have made as many such calculations (1 to 5) as there are spins in the lattice, we have completed one time unit, denoted as one Monte Carlo step per spin (MCS/spin). Apart from extreme cases, of the order of

10^3 Monte Carlo steps per spin are needed to get equilibrium averages; for the much more complicated spin glasses (where J is randomly positive or negative), relaxation times up to 10^7 MCS/spin have to be overcome.

Since the random number z is never larger than 1, any "probabilities" $p > 1$ arising from negative ΔE simply mean that we always flip the spin. In other words, if the energy would be lowered by the spin flip, we always flip and do not have to calculate a random number z. Instead of the probability $\exp(-\Delta E/k_B T)$ we may also use the properly normalized probability $1/(1 + \exp(\Delta E/k_B T))$ without changing the equilibrium results; at very high temperatures, $J/k_B T << 1$, this method converges much faster. It also avoids spurious chessboard–like patterns appearing sometimes with the other method if we go through a square lattice like a typewriter. With this second choice for the probability, we always have to calculate a random number to find out whether or not to flip.

```
      DIMENSION IS(8800),EX(13)
      DATA T,L,MAX,ISEED /4.5115,20,20,1/, IS/8800*1/
C     GIVE HERE TEMPERATURE IN UNITS OF J/KB, SIZE, TIME, SEED
      CALL RANSET(2*ISEED-1)
      L3=L*L*L
      L2=L*L
      L2P1=L2+1
      L3PL2=L3+L2
      M=L3/2
      DO 3 I=1,13,2
3     EX(I)=1.0/(1.0+EXP(2*(I-7)/T))
      DO 2 ITIME=1,MAX
      DO 1 K=L2P1,L3PL2
      ICI=IS(K)
      IF(EX(7+(IS(K-1)+IS(K+1)+IS(K-L)+IS(K+L)+IS(K-L2)+IS(K+L2))
1            *ICI).LT.RANF(K)) GOTO 1
      IS(K)=-ICI
      M=M-ICI
1     CONTINUE
      DO 4 K=1,L2
      IS(K)=IS(K+L3)
4     IS(K+L3PL2)=IS(K+L2)
2     PRINT *, M, ITIME
      DO 6 IZ=1,L
      PRINT 5, IZ
      DO 6 IY=1,L
      K=IZ*L2+IY*L-L
6     PRINT 5, (IS(K+IX),IX=1,L)
5     FORMAT(1,39I2)
      STOP
      END
```

To simulate physical processes best one should select randomly which spin is investigated next. However, computer time is saved if one goes through the lattice regularly. One may start with all spins up (for example, $S_k = 1$ for all k, $M = 1$) and watch how the magnetization M shrinks in the simulations. Instead one may start with the spins oriented randomly, $M = 0$, and check if M grows to a nonzero equilibrium value. The latter method takes more time but gives more interesting pictures at low temperatures and also results in domain growth. In equilibrium, both methods must converge to the same magnetization, apart from fluctuations.

The above program for zero magnetic field, which starts with all spins up, flips them with probability $1/(1 + \exp(\Delta E/k_B T))$, and shows a picture of the final configuration. We use a fast built–in random number generator RANF, which is initialized by RANSET with an odd integer as argument. Computer time is saved if we do not calculate the magnetization M (expressed here in units of $L^3/2$ for efficiency) at each step. More sophisticated "multi-spin coding" programs store many spins in one computer word (3 or 4 bits per spin) and thus save an order of magnitude in computer memory and a factor 2 and 3 in computer time. These techniques use even more heavily the bit–by–bit logical operations like the XOR described above in connection with the Kirkpatrick–Stoll random number generator. Since these Fortran elements are not standardized we refer the interested reader to the book by K.Binder [3].

The above method is often called after Metropolis [4] and describes the so–called Glauber dynamics, where the magnetization is not constant during the simulation. For fluids this means that particles can be created and annihilated at will, since we merely flip a spin. Physically that corresponds, for example, to the simulation of a small cube of air, where molecules are thought to scatter easily in and out of that volume because the boundaries exist only in the program, not in reality. Instead, one may also work with a constant number of particles, appropriate for a dense fluid, where each particle moves only from one site to a nearest neighbor site. Simulations of this so–called Kawasaki dynamics are more time consuming, but needed, for example, to study spinodal decomposition of binary systems.

What can a computer do with an Ising model? Ising himself solved the one–dimensional case; it shows no ferromagnetism at any nonzero temperature. The equilibrium properties in two dimensions were found exactly by Onsager and others. Thus three dimensions are the main problem where Monte Carlo solutions have been applied to bulk, surface and cluster properties. For example, the magnetization is greater than zero (more spins up than down) in zero magnetic field for temperatures below the Curie temperature T_c, and simulations showed $J/k_B T_c \approx 0.221654$, in agreement with other methods.

Near the Curie point, each spin strongly influences its neighbor, which influences its neighbor, which influences its neighbor, etc. The *correlation length* is the distance over which one spin appreciably influences other spins. It was found numerically to diverge for T near T_c as $|T - T_c|^{-\nu}$ with $\nu \approx 0.629$. This correlation length is of great practical importance for Monte Carlo simulations: It must be much smaller than the linear dimension L of the system if the simulation is supposed to give bulk properties. Any quantity X which behaves in an infinitely large system as $|T - T_c|^{-\gamma}$ will not diverge or vanish in a finite system with L^3 spins. Instead it varies at $T = T_c$ as $L^{\gamma/\nu}$ for large L. The magnetization M in zero field vanishes near the Curie point as $(T_c - T)^\beta$ in an infinite system, and therefore varies exactly at $T = T_c$ as $L^{-\beta/\nu}$. This "finite size scaling" method is an efficient tool to estimate critical exponents like y, provided one knows T_c very precisely: We simply vary the system size right at the critical point and get γ/ν from the asymptotic slope in a log–log plot. (Unfortunately, long relaxation times at T_c make this method less useful here than, e.g., for percolation.)

In addition one can also look at the dynamics: How long does it take for the magnetization M to reach its equilibrium value ? M as a function of time t (in MCS/spin) at $T = 1.4T_c$ is shown in Fig.1 (from Claus Kalle, 1983) for a $1080 * 1080 * 1080$ lattice, the largest three–dimensional system simulated to my knowledge thus far. Apart from an initial time lag, the data in this semilogarithmic plot follow a straight line, indicating a simple exponential decay $M(t) \sim \exp(-t/\tau)$. If we approach T_c this relaxation time τ diverges as $|T - T_c|^{-z\nu}$ in an infinite system. In a finite system at $T = T_c$ it varies as L^z according to finite size scaling, as discussed above. In three dimensions two different simulations gave z very close to 2. Also four– and five–dimensional systems have been studied. In two dimensions, where in contrast to equilibrium properties no exact solution has been found, we know $z \approx 2.14$ from Monte Carlo calculations. We will return to two–dimensional dynamics in the next section, where the more efficient Q2R algorithm is discussed.

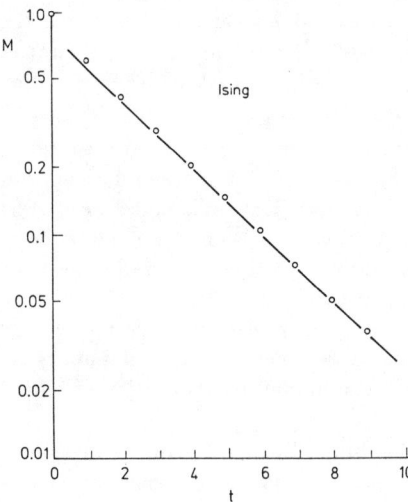

Fig. 1: Relaxation of magnetization for $T/T_c = 1.40$ in a 1080*1080*1080 simple cubic Ising lattice.

EXERCISE: a) Evaluate the magnetization for zero magnetic field in the three–dimensional Ising model as a function of temperature.

b) Where does the magnetization approach its equilibrium value faster: for temperatures slightly below or slightly above T_c ?

2.4 Cellular Automata (Q2R and Creutz)

In the simulations of the previous section we kept the temperature constant, and thus the energy fluctuated in the "canonical ensemble". Now we deal with "microcanonical" alternatives which keep the energy constant and thus have a fluctuating temperature. This method gives us an opportunity to introduce *deterministic cellular automata*. Those are lattices where each site k carries an integer variable S_k, called a spin, which has a limited number of values it can take. We let it be either -1 or $+1$ (or 0 and 1). The time t proceeds in steps of one and thus is also an integer. For time $t + 1$ the spin at site k gets a value determined uniquely from the spin values of its neighbors at time t, and in some models also from its own orientation $S_k(t)$ at time t. For example, on an $L*L$ square lattice with nearest neighbors $k - 1$, $k + 1$, $k - L$ and $k + L$ of site k (see Introduction), deterministic cellular automata are defined by the rule

$$S_k(t+1) = f_k[S_{k-1}(t), S_{k+1}(t), S_{k-L}(t), S_{k+L}(t), S_k(t)] \quad .$$

Each of the five spins in the argument of the rule f_k can point up or down ($S = 1$ or $= -1$) and thus can be in one of $2^5 = 32$ different configurations. For each of these 32 configurations the rule f_k can give for S_k the result up or the result down, which allows for $2^{32} = 4,294,967,296$ different rules. Even if we assume all sites of the lattice to obey the same rule, i.e. if f_k is independent of k, this variety allows me to write nearly 4300 million computer programs for this section. Constraints in time and money have prevented that; but the *Kauffman model* for genetics (see Sect.2.7) is just a random mixture of all possible rules, with each site selecting its rule independent of the others. In one dimension, on the other hand, with only a left and a right neighbor, the 2^8 rules for cellular automata have been studied systematically.

We now look for a rule f, identical for all sites, which approximates the Ising model (see preceding section). In the Ising model each spin tries to force its neighbor spins to be parallel to it (same value of the variable S_k). The only situation in which a spin is completely free to chose its direction is the case where it has as many neighbors pointing up as pointing down. If we flip a spin in such a situation, the total interaction energy with its neighbors will not be changed. Thus the *Q2R cellular automat* (so named by Gérard Vichniac [5]) obeys the rule:

A spin is flipped if and only if
it has as many up as down neighbors.

We therefore can program this model by going through the square lattice like a type-writer, check at every site if it has two up and two down neighbors, and if yes, flip the spin. We start now with a random configuration of spins, with each site having an up spin($S_k = 1$) with probability $1 - p$ and a down spin ($S_k = -1$) with probability p. Apart from these different initial conditions we could use the program at the end of the preceding (Ising) section and merely replace the long IF statement in the innermost loop there by

IF(IS(K−1)+IS(K+1)+IS(K−L)+IS(K+L)+IS(K−L2)+IS(K+L2).NE.0) GOTO 1

Here the underlined part is needed only in three dimensions. No random numbers are required except for the initialization, and thus the simulation is much faster than that for an Ising model.

While useful, this algorithm is not exactly the one usually studied in the literature, for it does not belong to cellular automata in the above sense. In cellular automata, a spin at time $t+1$ depends on the value its left and top (and also its other) neighbors had at time t, not at time $t+1$. If we go e.g. through a one–dimensional system then the above algorithm could flip, for example, spin 13 and then go to its right neighbor, spin 14. S_{14}, on the other hand, would now see the already flipped value of S_{13} and thus violate the traditional rule of simultaneous updating in cellular automata. One could store old and new configurations in two lattices, ISN(K) and IS(K), such that a spin flip means ISN(K)= −ICI and not IS(K)= −ICI in the Fortran program of Sect.3. After the loop has been completed one could insert a new loop equating the old with the new configuration: IS(K)=ISN(K). Now we have a proper cellular automat but one that violates the conservation of energy in the Ising model. Imagine all spins in a big latttice to be down, with the exception of four neighboring spins near the center which form a little square: $S_k = S_{k+1} = S_{k+L} = S_{k+L+1} = 1$ at time t. Since each of these 4 spins has two up and two down neighbors, they all will be flipped and thus down at time $t + 1$. No other spins will be flipped. The system has changed from one with a small domain of up spins in the center to a completely homogeneous lattice with all spins down. Clearly we have not kept the interaction energy constant in this process. More generally, in all simultaneous updating processes (also for multispin coding, for vector computers or for parallel computers) we have problems if interacting neighbors are treated simultaneously.

```
      DIMENSION IS(10098)
      DATA LHALF,MAX,ISEED,P/50,100,1,0.0795518/,IS/10098*1/
C     GIVE HERE L/2, TIME, MAX, SEED, CONCENTRATION
      L=2*LHALF
      LM1=L-1
      L2=LM1*L
      L2PL=L2+LM1
      CALL RANSET(2*ISEED-1)
      M=0
      DO 3 K=L,L2PL
      IF(RANF(K).LT.P) IS(K)=-1
3     M=M+IS(K)
      M=M/2
      DO 5 K=1,LM1
      IS(K)=IS(K+L2)
5     IS(K+L2PL)=IS(K+LM1)
      DO 2 ITIME=1,MAX
      DO 4 LATT=1,2
      KMIN=LM1+LATT
      KMAX=KMIN+L2-2
      DO 1 K=KMIN,KMAX,2
      IF(IS(K-1)+IS(K+1)+IS(K-LM1)+IS(K+LM1).NE.0) GOTO 1
      IS(K)=-IS(K)
      M=M+IS(K)
1     CONTINUE
      DO 4 K=1,LM1
      IS(K)=IS(K+L2)
4     IS(K+L2PL)=IS(K+LM1)
2     PRINT *, M,ITIME
      STOP
      END
```

The solution in the above program is simple for Q2R, and is standard also for the other (pseudo–)parallel processes: We divide the system into sublattices. Just as on a chessboard, we take half of the sites as "white" and the other half as "black" such that no sites of the same color are nearest neighbors. Then we treat first at time $t + 1/2$ the white sites, and after that at time $t + 1$ the black sites. On a lattice which is not exactly quadratic, for example with 100 lines of length 99, all the odd–numbered sites form one sublattice, and all the even numbered sites belong to the other sublattice. With this half–step separation the simultaneous updating in the Q2R model keeps the energy constant, and keeps the proper statistical weights if Ising models or similar cases are treated in parallel by multispin–coding or on vector computers. For Q2R it is a useful test for the correctness of the program to calculate the energy before and after the simulation by summing $S_i S_k$ over all neighbor pairs (i, k). That sum must be exactly the same; if it differs only slightly, then presumably the main algorithm is correct and only the boundary conditions are treated incorrectly.

The program simulates an $(L - 1) * L$ lattice with Q2R, with a concentration corresponding to the critical point of the two–dimensional Ising model. For smaller p we get a finite magnetization (given here in units of half the number of spins), for larger p the magnetization slowly approaches zero. L must be even so that $L - 1$ is odd; therefore we give LHALF as input value. The program runs faster if we calculate the magnetization only at the end.

If we want to run this program on a vector computer, we also omit the magnetization calculation in the innermost loop and write the IF–statement there as

IF(IS(K−1)+IS(K+1)+IS(K−LM1)+IS(K+LM1).EQ.0) IS(K)=−IS(K)

If the compiler refuses to vectorize this statement, and we cannot tell this stupid compiler that, because of our sublattice trick, there is no prohibited vector recursivity, then we beat the computer by storing the newly determined spins in a separate lattice ISN. Write ISN(K)=−IS(K) at the end of the IF–statement, and insert, after the end of loop 1, a new loop with IS(K)=ISN(K). Special care is now needed for the boundaries.

What can we do with Q2R cellular automata? They can be simulated very fast: Even when we store each spin in a separate computer word, as in the above program, the simulation is appreciably faster than that of a usual Ising model described in the previous section. The speed advantage increases if we use a vector computer (easy automatic vectorization of Q2R) or store each spin in one bit only. Combination of both techniques yielded speeds up to 6050 million steps per second.

Nevertheless, the magnetization calculated by Q2R in two and three dimensions agrees with that of the Ising model and vanishes at the same critical energy, within the numerical accuracy. Some other properties (like magnetization fluctuations) give difficulties, also the relaxation into equilibrium takes more Monte Carlo steps per spin than in the usual Ising model simulation. Nevertheless, Fig.2 shows at $T/T_c = 1.09$ the exponential relaxation of the magnetization with t in a 123008*123008 lattice, for much longer times than in Fig.1 at $T/T_c = 1.4$. But even in this very big system fluctuations finally become visible. Many aspects of Q2R cellular automata, like periods of limit cycles, are still an area of current research; periods up to 10^9 time units have been found. These periods are much smaller than 2^N in a square lattice of N spins; thus the algorithm is not *ergodic*, i.e. it does not visit all possible configurations of the system.

(To compare Ising and Q2R results we start with the thermal energy per site. In the two–dimensional Ising model this energy is known exactly as a function of temperature, in three dimensions its relation to temperature is known numerically. For Q2R the thermal energy remains constant in the simulation and thus equals the energy at the initialization of the spin orientation. On average it equals $2Jqp(1 - p)$ where $2J$ is the energy to break a single bond and q the number of neighbors of each lattice site. Thus in the square lattice, where the critical thermal energy is $(2 - \sqrt{2})J$, the critical concentration p_c is 7.95518 % since $q = 4$; in the simple cubic lattice, $p_c \approx 21.25$ %. It seems impossible to include an

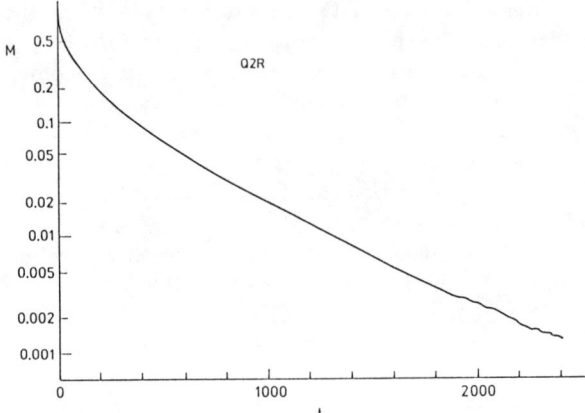

Fig.2: Relaxation of magnetization at $T/T_c = 1.092$ in a $123008 * 123008$ square Q2R lattice.

arbitrary magnetic field in the Q2R algorithm.)

Since 1982 Creutz [6] has invented other algorithms for Ising model simulations at constant energy, which are more complicated, but more realistic and in better agreement with the true Ising results. One can assign a "demon" to each site which can store a limited amount of energy. A spin is flipped if and only if the energy change is compatible with the energy reservoir of the demon. That means the spin energy can be increased if the demon can lend this energy to the spin from the demon energy reservoir. In this sense the demon acts like a checking account at a bank. It is even possible for all spins to share such a bank account, i.e. a demon runs through the lattice and flips a spin if and only if the energy change is compatible with the current energy in the demon energy reservoir. The Ising program of the preceding section is changed into one with a demon by replacing the IF statement in the center loop 1 by

```
IDNEW=ID-(IS(K-1)+IS(K+1)+IS(K-L)+IS(K+L)+IS(K-L2)+IS(K+L2))*ICI
IF(IDNEW.LT.0) GOTO 1
ID=IDNEW
```

where ID and IDNEW are the demon energies in units of $2J$. (Initially, ID$= 0$ and the spins are distributed up and down with probability p, as for Q2R.) Omitting these demons means a return to Q2R. Of course, with a running demon the Creutz algorithm is no longer a cellular automat. With fixed demons it is such an automat, but with more than one bit information per site: Besides the spin we also have the demon energy there as a variable.

EXERCISE: Find the magnetization as a function of temperature for Q2R on the square lattice.

2.5 Diffusion and Percolation

If this writer leaves, completely drunk, the "Metropole" bar in mid–town Manhattan to find his hotel, at each street corner he forgets where he came from and selects at random the direction in which he now goes. The center of New York is approximately a square lattice, and thus it is faster (though not as enjoyable for some) to simulate this diffusion process on a computer. Molecules in the air also diffuse: After every scattering with another molecule, they fly roughly straight ahead for a distance of the order of 10^{-7} meters and then are scattered again by another molecule. Since this other molecule is barely correlated with the first one, the scattering directions can be taken as random. Small particles in a liquid, viewed under a microscope, move in a similar way, called Brownian motion after its first observer. Thus on a lattice, diffusion is defined as the process whereby at each site a random walker selects randomly to which of the nearest neighbor sites he moves next.

How do we program diffusion on a square lattice. An obvious but inefficient way, where RANF gives a random number < 1, would be to change the x and y coordinates of the walker as follows.

```
      DO 1 ITIME=1,MAX
      Z=RANF(ITIME)
      IF                 (Z.LT.0.25) X=X+1
      IF(Z.GE.0.25.AND.Z.LT.0.50) X=X-1
      IF(Z.GE.0.50.AND.Z.LT.0.75) Y=Y+1
1     IF(Z.GE.0.75)               Y=Y-1
```

Here we used four IF-statements, which require the computer to think, not to calculate. And thinking is not what modern number crunchers do best. Usually a computer makes faster a simple calculation than a decision whether or not the result is needed. Humans act the opposite way, and the above program is more human thinking than efficient Fortran.

It is in general faster to use (see Introduction) one-dimensional storage of the L*L lattice and to store the resulting neighbor distances in a small array NB(4) with the four distances:

```
      NB(1)= 1
      NB(2)=-1
      NB(3)= L
      NB(4)=-L
      DO 1 ITIME=1,MAX
1     K=K+NB(1+IFIX(4.0*RANF(ITIME)))
```

If after hundreds of time steps we want to know the X and Y coordinate hidden in the combined coordinate K, we get them via integer divisions or modulo functions: $Y = (K - 1)/L$ and $X = K - L * Y$. If we touch the upper or lower boundary, we stop the simulation or use periodic boundary conditions: $K = K \pm L^2$.

In a finite lattice, of course, the distances from the origin will always be finite in this way. "Infinite" distances even in a finite lattice can be reached if, instead of moving K, we merely count how often we move up, down, left and right. The complete program then could look like:

```
      DIMENSION IDIST(4)
      DATA MAX/1000/,IDIST/4*0/
      DO 1 ITIME=1,MAX
      INDEX=1+IFIX(4.0*RANF(ITIME))
1     IDIST(INDEX)=IDIST(INDEX)+1
      R2=(IDIST(1)-IDIST(2))**2 + (IDIST(3)-IDIST(4))**2
      PRINT *, R2, MAX
      STOP
      END
```

A line K=K+NB(INDEX) could be added to this loop but is not really needed. Averaging over many such runs the programmer will hopefully note that the mean square displacement $< R^2 >$ equals the number MAX of time steps.

However, this result can be derived exactly without any help from computers. Then, what do we need computers for, except to show nice pictures with high–resolution graphics? Let us combine diffusion with another random process, *percolation*. In percolation theory, each site of a lattice is occupied randomly with probability p and empty with probability $1 - p$; a cluster is a group of occupied neighbors. Now we let the random walker move only on the occupied sites, never on the empty places of this percolation problem. De Gennes called this problem the ant in the labyrinth. By definition, the ant is restricted in its walk to the cluster on which it first landed.

Thus we first occupy each lattice site k with probability p by setting IS(K)=1 with probability p and $= 0$ otherwise (compare with loop 3 in the Q2R program of the preceding section). Then the innermost loop is

```
        DO 1 ITIME=1,MAX
        INDEX=1+IFIX(4.0*RANF(ITIME))
        KNEW=K+NB(INDEX)
        IF(IS(KNEW).EQ.0) GOTO 1
        K=KNEW
        IDIST(INDEX)=IDIST(INDEX)+1
   1    CONTINUE
```

A time consuming check for periodic boundary conditions can be avoided by adding a completely empty buffer line to the top of the lattice, and another such buffer to the bottom. Then the ant never moves there and never tries to look into a non–existing neighbor.

If we vary the concentration p of allowed sites, we will find that for small p the ant moves very little. For p near unity, on the other hand, it diffuses with $< distance^2 >$ proportional to time. The border concentration p_c is called the percolation threshold and is about 0.592746 on the square lattice and about 0.3116 on the simple cubic lattice. For $p < p_c$ all clusters are finite; for $p > p_c$ we find in addition one infinite cluster on which an ant can travel to infinity. There are more efficient ways to check for infinite clusters than letting ants diffuse in the labyrinth; clusters have been counted in lattices as large as 160000*160000 by an algorithm too complicated for these lectures.

Letting ants diffuse at $p = p_c$ we will find many walks trapped into a finite cluster and thus limited in their distance. Some of them will start on the infinite cluster and move to "infinity". Averaging over all such random walks, the mean square distance $< R^2 >$ varies as t^{2k}; $1/k$ is also called the fractal dimension of the walk. For $p < p_c$ we have $k = 0$, for $p > p_c$ normal diffusion with $k = 1/2$ prevails, and at $p = p_c$ we find anomalous diffusion witk k near 0.19 in three dimensions. Such behavior of critical exponents (one value on one side, another value on the other side, and a third type of behavior right at the transition) is quite common for dynamical phenomena near critical points.

Numerically in three dimensions, the effective exponent k for intermediate times is larger than the limiting $k \approx 0.19$ for infinitely long times. High accuracy simulations also require large lattices; simulations have been made with a vectorized program and single–bit storage of 376*376*376 lattices, performing 4.4 million steps per second, Fig.3. But also on smaller computers one can find numerically the difference in the behavior below, at and above the percolation threshold. In 1982 such type of research became very fashionable [7].

A theorem due to Einstein relates the diffusivity to the electrical conductivity if the diffusors are electrons; thus our simulations measure also conductivity in disordered systems.

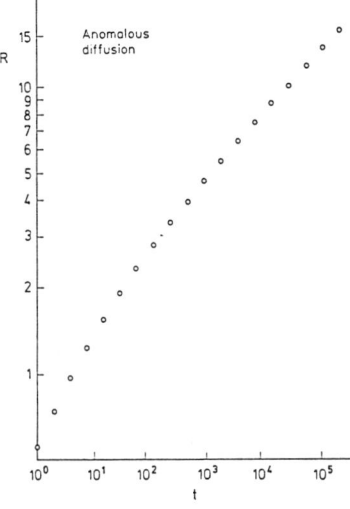

Fig. 3: Log-log plot of distance R versus time t, for diffusion at the percolation threshold, $p = 0.3116$, in 376*376*376 simple cubic lattice. Averages over 1500 lattices with 512 diffusors each.

EXERCISE: Find on the square lattice at $p = p_c = 0.592746$ the long–time limit of $< distance^2 > /t^{2/3}$.

2.6 Eden Clusters

In 1961, Eden [8] published a simple model for *tumor growth* which lay nearly dormant for many years until cluster growth and fractal surface properties became fashionable in computational physics after 1981. We use this model here as a particularly simple growth process, ignoring its possible biological applications.

Let us start at time $t = 1$ with the site in the center of a large lattice occupied, and all other sites empty. At each time step from t to $t + 1$ we occupy exactly one site; this site is selected randomly from all perimeter sites at time t. A perimeter site is an empty site which has at least one occupied neighbor. For this simple *Eden model*, these perimeter sites constitute the surface of the cluster constructed randomly in this way. Once we have occupied the new site k, we have to check all its neighbors: If they are already occupied or perimeter sites, then their status remains unchanged; if the neighbor site was neither occupied nor classified as perimeter before, we mark them as perimeter sites and adjust the number IP of perimeter sites accordingly. We list below a short program for the square lattice (RANF selects a random number < 1 and is initialized by RANSET).

In this Eden program we start with time $t = 0$ where no site is occupied and the center site KCENT is defined as a perimeter site. The number IP of perimeter sites equals unity at the beginning. Thus in the next time step, $t = 1$, the center site will necessarily be occupied, and its neighbors will become perimeter sites. The loop from *itime* $= 1$ to *itime* $= max$ then selects randomly from the list ISURF of perimeter sites the new site K= ISURF(I) to be occupied and removes this site from the perimeter list. For the latter purpose we store the coordinates of the last perimeter site ISURF(IP) in the surface list at that place I, where we had previously stored the coordinates of the now occupied place. We then reduce the number IP of perimeter sites by one.

```
          DIMENSION ISURF(600),LATT(6241),NB(4)
          DATA LHALF,MAX,ISEED/39,1000,1/, LATT/6241*1/
   C      GIVE HERE L/2, TIME, SEED
          CALL RANSET(2*ISEED-1)
          L=LHALF*2+1
          KCENT=1+LHALF*(L+1)
          NB(1)= 1
          NB(2)=-1
          NB(3)= L
          NB(4)=-L
          ISURF(1)=KCENT
          LATT(KCENT)=0
          IP=1
          DO 1 ITIME=1,MAX
          I=1+IFIX(RANF(ITIME)*IP)
          K=ISURF(I)
          ISURF(I)=ISURF(IP)
          IP=IP-1
          DO 1 INB=1,4
          KNEW=K+NB(INB)
          IF(LATT(KNEW).EQ.0) GOTO 1
          LATT(KNEW)=0
          IP=IP+1
          ISURF(IP)=KNEW
   1      CONTINUE
   2      FORMAT(1X,79I1)
          PRINT 2, LATT
          STOP
          END
```

Now the innermost loop looks into the four neighbors KNEW=K + NB(INB) of the newly occupied site. If that site has already been investigated before, it is either a perimeter or an occupied site and thus does not change our list of perimeter sites; sites which have been investigated before are marked by a zero in an array LATT representing the whole lattice. If, on the other hand, LATT equals the value 1 it got at the start of the simulation (DATA statement), then we mark the neighbor as a perimeter site, in three steps: We set LATT=0 since now this site has been treated; we increase IP by one; and we store the coordinate KNEW of this neighbor site in the list ISURF of perimeter sites as ISURF(IP).

At the end we print the 79*79 array LATT which makes the cluster visible. Of course the size MAX of the cluster should be chosen small enough so that no cluster site touches the boundaries of the lattice; periodic boundary conditions make little sense for the growth of a round cluster. In addition one could print out, as a function of time, the number IP of perimeter sites, their average distance $< R >$ from the origin KCENT, and the fluctuations $W^2 =< R^2 > - < R >^2$ of that distance. Of course, to simulate larger clusters we can store bitwise the information in LATT, whether or not that site has been investigated before. Some execution time may be saved if we "unroll" the loop DO 1 INB=1,4 by writing the statements within the loop four times, for each neighbor explicitly. Nevertheless, it is difficult to use this algorithm on a supercomputer efficiently, since these computers require "vectorization" (see appendix).

Over the last ten years research has shown that on the square lattice the average number of perimeter sites as well as the average radius $< R >$ increase as the square root of time, i.e. as the square root of the number of occupied sites. In other words, Eden clusters are not fractal. We see that result also from the computer printout of the shape of a sufficiently large cluster: Nearly all sites in the cluster interior are occupied, and the cluster forms roughly a compact circle. The interesting information is hidden in the width W of the surface layer, defined above. This width increases in a complicated way with the number of occupied sites; only when more then 50 million sites have been occupied is W proportional to the square root of the number of occupied sites, Fig.4. This proportionality is expected because of a slight lattice anisotropy. To find the asymptotic behavior in three and four dimensions, it was useful to introduce the trick of "noise reduction" where a site is occupied only after it has been selected m times by the random number generator, with $m = 1$ corresponding to the normal Eden model and very large m removing nearly all fluctuation effects from the surface. Research is still going on in this field, and no theory is known to us which successfully describes the numerically observed variation with dimensionality. Thus while the Eden model is particularly simple to describe and program, it is particularly difficult to interpret correctly.

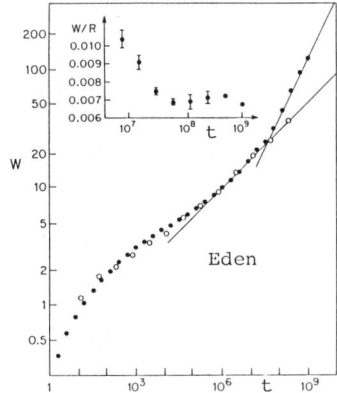

Fig.4: Log–log plot of surface width W versus time t for two–dimensional Eden clusters (full dots) . The open dots correspond to a flat surface simulation: no lattice anisotropy.

This Eden model can be varied in lots of ways, and there are many other types of cluster growth models which have been simulated on a computer. For all of them one can check how the radius increases with increasing "mass" , i.e. with the number of occupied sites. In a power–law relation: mass $\sim$ (radius)^D one then calls D the *fractal dimension* of the cluster growth process. In Eden clusters the fractal dimension D equals the dimensionality d of the lattice since interior sites tend to be filled up. In many other growing clusters, D is smaller than d. This fractal dimension D is a unifying concept in describing quantitatively an important aspect of the growth process, whether they are simulated clusters, clouds, or urban agglomerations.

Recent years have seen an enormous research effort on cluster growth. Presumably the most famous examples are the diffusion limited aggregates (DLA), where we occupy one perimeter site at each time step, just as for the Eden model. However, that site is not selected randomly with equal probability from all perimeter sites, but instead selected by a small test particle which is diffusing in the free space around the cluster and selects a perimeter site by hitting it in this diffusion process.

EXERCISE: Find for large Eden clusters the ratio of the number of perimeter sites to the number of occupied sites on the square lattice.

2.7 Kauffman Model

Stuart Kauffman [9] suggested in 1969 a computer model to simulate *genetic systems*. Human beings have about $N = 10^6$ genes, which can be switched either on or off. That would allow for $2^N = 10^{300000}$ different cell types in one single human being. Actually one finds only about 10^3 different cell types; presumably life would be quite difficult to organize if we had too many different cell types. Kauffman makes interactions between different genes responsible for the reduction in the variety of life. Similarly, a system of N spins which can be on or off has 2^N different configurations. At low temperatures, however, only two of them are important if ferromagnetic interactions force neighboring spins to be parallel. In genetics we need a model in between these two extremes: 2^N is too large, and 2 is too small for the number of different cell types.

Thus Kauffman uses the most disordered "cellular automat" (see Sect. 4) as a genetic model: Each site of a square lattice carries a "spin" which is either up or down and which is influenced by its 4 neighbors. The spin orientation at time $t + 1$ is determined completely by the orientation of the 4 neighbors at time t. The rule according to which the 4 neighbors influence their central spin varies from site to site and is taken randomly from the pool of $2^{16} = 65536$ possible rules. For example, one spin may be up if and only if all its 4 neighbors are up; the next spin may be up if and only if 2 neighbors are down and 2 are up, etc. Clearly, a realistic model for life should not assume that living cells and their genes are produced all alike in a computer chip factory; the extremely disordered Kauffman model might be more realistic in this respect.

(Kauffman studied primarily the case where each site interacts with other sites anywhere in the lattice. Many aspects of this infinite–range model can be solved exactly without computer simulations; thus we use here nearest–neighbor interactions as the other extreme. Besides square lattices, also triangular or simple cubic lattices have been studied.)

Out of this disordered structure, some order arises. That, of course, is the nature of life, which supports this moderately ordered writer with a random mixture of H_2O, C_2H_5OH and less important chemicals. If we simulate two different Kauffman lattices with the same set of rules for each corresponding site, but completely uncorrelated initial distributions of spin orientations, then after some time t we will find, by putting the two lattices on top of each other, that the proportion of parallel spins has become slightly higher than that of antiparallel spins. Thus the identity of the two sets of rules produces no complete identity, but at least some similarity, of the configurations arising out of these rules. The following program gives the number of up spins in a 40*40 Kauffman lattice, as a function of time.

Now we describe the programming technique, introducing an additional parameter p, which was 1/2 in the above description. At the beginning, how do we tell each site to select randomly from the set of 65536 possible rules ? We go through the lattice like a typewriter and thus treat each site separately. If each site has 4 neighbors with a spin IS which is 1 (up) or 0 (down), then there are $2^4 = 16$ possible configurations for these neighbors. For each of them we fix randomly whether the result for the central spin at the next time step should be up or down. Thus the sequence of 16 different numbers 0 or 1 fixes the rule for that site. We denote the neighbor configuration of site k by an index ranging from 1 to 16:

INDEX=1+IS(K–1)+IS(K+1)*2+IS(K–L)*4+IS(K+L)*8

Thus for the initialization we take the rule array LAW(INDEX,K) randomly as 0 or 1, for index from 1 to 16, and for all sites k. We also let the spins randomly point up or down. In the program this initialization is done in loop 3, where RANF gives a random number < 1, and RANSET initializes RANF. (Note that 0.5+RANF, rounded downward to an integer, gives 0 and 1 with probability 1/2, as desired.)

```
      DIMENSION LAW(16,1680),IS(1680),ISN(1680)
      DATA L,MAX,ISEED,P/40,100,1,0.29/
C     GIVE HERE SIZE, TIME, SEED, CONCENTRATION
      L2=L*L
      LP1=L+1
      L2PL=L2+L
      CALL RANSET(2*ISEED-1)
      PP1=P+1.0
      DO 3 K=LP1,L2PL
      IS(K)=0.5+RANF(K)
      DO 3 INDEX=1,16
C3    LAW(K)= IFIX(PP1-RANF(INDEX)).OR.SHIFT(LAW(K),1)
    3 LAW(INDEX,K)=PP1-RANF(INDEX)
      DO 2 ITIME=1,MAX
      DO 5 K=1,L
      IS(K)=IS(K+L2)
    5 IS(K+L2PL)=IS(K+L)
      DO 1 K=LP1,L2PL
C1    ISN(K)=1.AND.SHIFT(LAW(K),
C   1       -IS(K-1)-IS(K+1)*2-IS(K-L)*4-IS(K+L)*8)
    1 ISN(K)=LAW(1+IS(K-1)+IS(K+1)*2+IS(K-L)*4+IS(K+L)*8, K)
      M=0
      DO 4 K=LP1,L2PL
      M=M+ISN(K)
    4 IS(K)=ISN(K)
    2 PRINT *, M,ITIME
      STOP
      END
```

To get more parameters to work with, we make "up rules" less probable than "down rules". Thus in the initialization loop 3, the rule LAW is taken as 1 with probability p, and as 0 with probability $1 - p$; the reader can easily check that we get this result if we round $p + 1 - $RANF downward to an integer, as done in the last line of loop 3. Note that this probability p still leaves the Kauffman model completely deterministic: Once the initialization of spins IS and rules LAW is completed, the whole future development is fixed.

This future development is now easily found by calculating for every site K the current neighbor configuration; thus we calculate the above index between 1 and 16. Then we set the new spin value ISN(K) equal to LAW(INDEX,K). Actually it is not even necessary to store the current INDEX value as a variable. After all new spins have been determined, we replace the old orientations by the new ones in loop 4: IS(K)=ISN(K). Loop 5 updates the two buffer lines.

Memory can be saved by storing many sites IS and rules LAW in one computer word. Since most of the memory is used for LAW, the Kauffman model offers an alternative which makes vectorization for supercomputers easier (no "gather" needed): Within one word for LAW we store all 16 values given by the rule for that site for the 16 different neighbor configurations. Thus we use the 16 least significant bits of the computer word LAW. If we want to read off the bit in LAW(K) corresponding to the neighbor configuration INDEX, we shift LAW by INDEX-1 bits to the right and read off the last bit by a logical AND with 1. On a CDC scalar computer this shifting and reading is accomplished if in the above program we replace two lines by those written above them with the "comment" mark C in their first column. (On other computers we may divide an integer number by 2^n in order to shift it to the right by n bits.) In the DIMENSION statement, the first index for LAW now can be omitted. (Storing each site IS in one bit and using only logical bit-by-bit operations in a different algorithm, 60 million updates per second were reached on a Cray vector computer.)

What do we find from such simulations ? Observing long rows of numbers of up spins as a function of time we find that for small p these numbers repeat themselves after short periods. For large p no such periods are visible except for very small systems. (Of course, N spins cannot have any period longer than 2^N.) Large p here means p near 0.5 since p and $1-p$ are equivalent. It seems that for large p the periods increase exponentially with lattice size N, for small p the increase is much weaker. The transition between these two regimes, i.e., the critical value p_c, can be determined more accurately by checking for the "damage" created by a "mutation" in the genetic system simulated by the Kauffman model. How does a single violation of the rules affect the configuration evolving later ? To check this we simulate two nearly identical Kauffman lattices: Each site in one lattice has exactly the same rule as the corresponding site in the other lattices and has the same initial spin orientation as the corresponding spin in the other lattice. Then, at time $t = 0$, we flip the center spin in one lattice but not in the other, and call that flip a mutation. Now we simulate both lattices by the Kauffman rules and compare site by site where the two configurations differ in the spin orientation. The set of differing spins can be called the later damage caused by the initial mutation. We check in particular whether the damage remains limited or spreads over a finite fraction of the whole system. In other words, is the genetic system stable against a small mutation, as required for life, or can a small error destroy the whole genetic make-up ?

It turns out that for $p < p_c$ the damage remains limited whereas for $p > p_c$ it spreads over the whole lattice. The threshold p_c is near 0.3 in the square lattice and smaller for the triangular or simple cubic lattice. Figure 5 shows how long it takes at $p = p_c$ for the damage to touch the boundaries of an L*L lattice, and how many sites are damaged at the moment of touching. The slopes in these log-log plots can be called fractal dimensions of time and mass. Instead of "damage" we can also use "Hamming distance" and relate it to the "overlap" of the two configurations. After Kauffman such damage spreading was also studied in cellular automata like Q2R, in Ising ferromagnets and in spin glasses. Such studies correspond to stability analysis in systems with continuous variables, like in classical me-

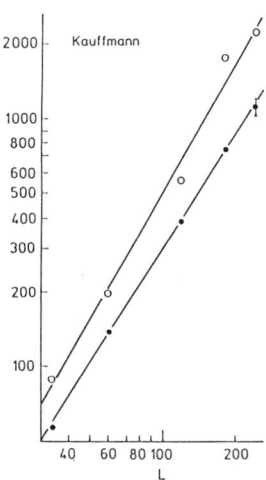

Fig. 5: Log-log plot of time for damage to touch the boundary (dots) and damage at touching time (crosses), versus size L of Kauffman square lattice, for $p = p_c = 0.29$. Initially only the center is damaged.

chanics or numerical mathematics. While the biological significance of the Kauffman model is beyond this writer's competence, it certainly is a computational challenge, particularly near p_c. And the questions asked in the Kauffman model are spilling over to other fields of statistical physics. Readers interested in other computer simulations of possible biological significance might like to study models for neural networks, for evolutions, or most recently for immunology [10].

EXERCISE: Check for many independent runs of Kauffman models if periodic oscillations of the number of up spins occur, and determine this period for $p = 0.1$ and $p = 0.5$ on the square lattice.

2.8 Summary

The reader may have noticed that this chapter has used "primitive" and not "structured" programming. Apart from single–bit handling, it should be easy to transfer the programs to other computers and languages like Basic or Pascal; we did not even use the extensions of Fortran 77 over Fortran 66. This was possible since all programs were short; if instead one deals with programs of thousands of lines and numerous people working with them over many years, then we must use structured programming with many independent subroutines and careful documentation. The present writer prefers steak over quiche and thus likes programs to be printed on one page, giving one line of output after one night of execution time. Of course, this ideal is not always reached: In applications of the above programs, more program lines would be added to analyze the quantities of interest. And if then the program becomes too long to be listed for each run, one should print out at the beginning all input parameters, including the random number seed.

These lectures also did not deal with the problems modern computing can create in society. Obviously a faster simulation of an Ising model does not make a physicist unemployed, since in the pre–computer age universities did not employ physicists to flip millions of spins by hand. For computerized text processing, the rationalization effects are different. The greatest dangers from Eden tumor simulations seem to be stomach ulcers for the simulators, while military applications of computing will be presumably crucial for World War III (and irrelevant the day after).

2.9 Appendix: Principles of Vector Computing

Present "supercomputers" like CDC Cyber 205, the Cray series, the ETA 10, the IBM 3090 with vector feature, but also "Crayettes" like the Convex, are vector computers. In principle it is wrong to describe them as parallel computers, which are mostly still under development. In practice, however, they can be treated as if they perform numerous identical calculations in parallel, i.e., simultaneously.

How can vector computers achieve greater efficiency even if they have only one central processing unit like most "scalar" (i.e. not vectorizing) computers. Imagine we need to compute

```
        DO 1 I=1,200
  1     A(I)=B(I)+C(I)*D(I)
```

A normal scalar computer would have to go, repeatedly for 200 values of I, roughly through the following steps: 1) Calculate the "address" (position in computer memory) of B_i, C_i and D_i. 2) Get the values of B_i, C_i and D_i from the computed adresses in the main memory into those storage areas ("registers") where they can be used for calculations. 3) Multiply C_i with D_i and add the result to B_i. 4) Calculate the address of A_i. 5) Store there the result of the calculation. 6) Increase I by 1 and stop if then I>200.

Obviously, this computation takes some time, since steps 1 and 2 consist each of three parts. The method described above corresponds to the nineteenth–century way of building cars. Modern cars, however, are built on assembly lines, where numerous different tasks are performed simultaneously on different cars, with the result that every time unit one car is rolling off the assembly line. Vector computers do for numbers what assembly lines do for cars, except that experts talk about "pipelines" instead of "assembly lines". Of course, assembly lines have their disadvantage: You cannot ask to get a Cadillac if you are standing by a Ford Company assembly line. You cannot drive around in car number 100 to fetch the parts needed to start construction of cars number 99 or 98. You have to keep your supplies in such an order that you simply take the next part off the shelf if you start working on the next car. And it is not useful to build an assembly line if one wants to construct only 4 cars.

Vector computers work similarly: One should compute the same expressions for the different elements, i.e. for I between 1 and 200. One cannot use element A_{i-1} in the computation of element A_i. The data to be treated consecutively should be stored in consecutive elements of the computer memory. Loops to be vectorized should have a minimum length of about 50. In the above example, these four conditions are fulfilled, and the computer loves to vectorize this loop, i.e. to produce the data on its assembly line . At the time where the computer takes the value of D_{100} from the memory, it also multiplies C_{99} with D_{99}, looks up the value of B_{98}, adds $C_{97} * D_{97}$ to B_{97}, and stores the previously calculated result $B_{96} + C_{96} * D_{96}$ in the memory. Calculations of addresses are needed only at the beginning since all required data are stored consecutively in the memory. In this way, for each cycle of the computer, one element A_i is calculated and stored. Computer time may have decreased by one order of magnitude for this loop.

The sum $\sum_i A_i$ which is usually calculated through

```
          SUM=0.0
          DO 2 I=1,200
   2      SUM=SUM+A(I)
```

cannot be vectorized since the value for this sum after the 100–th addition is needed already for the 101–th addition and is not yet known at that time $i = 101$. Nevertheless, vector computers have efficient built–in routines to do such sums, and the user should utilize them to gain speed; modern supercomputers recognize these sums automatically.

Unfortunately, Monte Carlo simulations in statistical physics require loops which are more complicated, and it could be a big problem to produce random numbers in a vectorized fashion. More importantly, one needs these random numbers to control the flow of the data or statements. Let us assume, for example, that in the diffusion–percolation problem

```
          DO 1 ITIME=1,MAX
          KNEW=K+NB(1+4*RANF(ITIME))
   1      IF(IS(KNEW).NE.0) K=KNEW
```

we have been able to produce MAX different random numbers between 0 and 1, stored as RANF(ITIME). Then the computer needs the data NB, not at consecutive memory addresses, but from positions 1+4*RANF scattered randomly in (a small section of) the memory. One first has to gather these data together in such a way that finally an array NBG contains them in the desired order:

$$NBG(ITIME)=NB(1+4*RANF(ITIME))$$

Such GATHER requirements for this so–called indirect adressing are done automatically on modern supercomputers and must be inserted manually by the user for older vector compilers; in both cases they slow down appreciably the computation. (The opposite of GATHER is called SCATTER and is needed for a statement of the type A(I(J))=B(I). Some compilers do it automatically.)

Having overcome the gather problem, we still cannot vectorize

```
          DO 1 ITIME=1,200
          NBG(ITIME)=1+NB(4*RANF(ITIME))
          KNEW=K+NBG(ITIME)
   1      IF(IS(KNEW(ITIME).NE.0) K=KNEW
```

in our diffusion process. For obviously each new position K+NBG depends on the position K in the previous step. The old K has not yet been calculated and stored when it is needed for K+NBG, thus vectorization with respect to ITIME is not possible. However, in most applications we will simulate more than one random walk. Let us assume that N walkers run around on the same disordered lattice. On a scalar computer we then will put an outermost loop DO 9 IWALK = 1,N around the whole simulation. On a vector computer we put this loop inside:

```
          DO 1 ITIME=1,200
          DO 9 IWALK=1,N
          NBG(IWALK)=NB(1+4*RANF(IWALK))
          KNEW(IWALK)=K(IWALK)+NBG(IWALK)
   9      IF(IS(KNEW(IWALK)).NE.0) K(IWALK)=KNEW(IWALK)
   1      CONTINUE
```

In other words, we vectorize with respect to IWALK, not with respect to ITIME. Now the innermost loop can be vectorized, though for IS(KNEW(IWALK)) we need another GATHER operation. Unfortunately, we now need much more memory space for the arrays KNEW(IWALK) and K(IWALK), which before where only single variables. Quite generally, vector computing often requires many arrays where before single variables were sufficient. The trick to exchange outer and inner loop is widespread in vector computing; some compilers even do it automatically in simple cases.

The reader may wonder why I claimed the IF–statement at the end to be vectorizable. Most vector computers allow vectorization of IF–conditions via a simple trick: The computer always performs all the computations after the IF–statement, whether the IF gives "true" or "false"; only at the very end, the results are stored only if the condition was "true", and thrown away if the condition was "false". If in half the cases the condition is fulfilled one wastes half of the effort, but gains much more in efficiency. The trick is more problematic if in only one percent of the cases the condition is fulfilled, and 99 % of the calculations are thrown away. Some vector computers may even understand that a GO TO statement jumping several lines ahead is merely a vectorizable IF–condition. However, a GO TO jump backwards cannot be vectorized.

The more complicated the innermost loop is, the smaller is the chance that it can be vectorized. Input–output statements or other complicated functions and subroutines cannot be vectorized. Keeping in mind what is possible and what not on an assembly line the programmer may check how many complications are needed before his innermost loop can be vectorized. If too many GATHER and SCATTER calls are needed, or if memory requirements become too large, it may be best not to use a vector computer for this purpose. A Cray can be much faster than a scalar computer, just as an airplane is in general faster than a car. However, airplanes are not the most efficient, albeit possible, way to get from Kennedy airport to La Guardia airport within New York City; cars are better suited for that purpose.

For the examples in the earlier sections, information about vector programming is published, e.g., in the following references: Random numbers: J.Stat.Phys. 34, 427 (1984) (also for diffusion, sect.5) and Comp.Phys.Comm.33, 343 (1984); Ising model: J.Stat.Phys. 37, 217 (1984); Q2R automata: J.Stat.Phys. 45, 145 (1986); Eden growth: Phys.Rev. A 34, 1523 (1986); Kauffman model: J.Stat.Phys. (1988) (da Silva and Herrmann).

EXERCISE: Program the matrix multiplication $C_{ik} = \sum_j A_{ij} B_{jk}$ in a vectorizable form without using a fast built–in summation routine. (Trick: Exchange outer and inner loop.)

2.10 References

[1] D.W. Heermann, *Computer Simulation Methods in Statistical Physics*, Springer Verlag, Berlin, Heidelberg, New York 1986
[2] S.Kirkpatrick, E.P.Stoll, J.Comp.Phys. 40, 517 (1980)
[3] K. Binder (ed.), *Applications of the Monte Carlo Method in Statistical Physics*, Springer Verlag, Berlin, Heidelberg, New York 1984, Chap.1 . See also the textbook: K.Binder and D.W.Heermann, *Monte Carlo Simulation in Statistical Physics: An Introduction*, Springer Verlag, Berlin, Heidelberg, New York, in press, which is suited as a follow-up on the present chapter for the more advanced student.
[4] N.Metropolis, A.W.Rosenbluth, M.N.Rosenbluth, A.H.Teller, E.Teller, J.Chem.Phys. 21, 1087 (1953)
[5] G.Y.Vichniac, Physica D 10, 96 (1984)
[6] M.Creutz, Phys.Rev.Letters 50, 1411 (1983)
[7] D.Stauffer, *Introduction to Percolation Theory*, Taylor and Francis, London 1985
[8] M.Eden, in: *Proc. 4th Berkeley Symp. Math.Statist. and Probability*, ed. F.Neyman, vol.IV, University of California, Berkeley 1961
[9] S.A.Kauffman, J.Theor.Biol. 22, 437 (1969)
[10] G.Weisbuch, H.Atlan, J.Phys. A 21, L 189 (1988)

Notes Added to the Second Edition

An earlier reference than ref. 8 is M. Eden, in: *Symp. on Information Theory in Biology*, ed. H.P. Yockey, Pergamon Press, New York 1958, page 359.

For the advanced reader interested in the multi-spin coding technique mentioned on page 63, we give below the complete program for a 800*800 Ising model on the square lattice. This ran on a 32 bit IBM mainframe, with 8 spins per word. It uses exclusive-or (IEOR), logical and (IAND) and shift (ISHFT) on a bit-by-bit basis. To understand these tricks one should first read loop 5 where the number M of up spins (one bits) is calculated: We go through all spin words IS and then for each of them check in all eight bits representing the spin whether the bit is zero or one, by a logical and with the number 1. Loop 3 costs most of the time and tries to flip each of the 8 spins in the word ICI separately. The changer word ICH is marked with a one bit wherever a spin is to be flipped. The four exclusive-ors in the lines before loop 3 give the number of antiparallel neighbours in the four lattice directions. We use free boundary conditions in the multi-spin direction, and periodic ones in the other direction. The number 0.440687 is $J/k_B T_c$. There are faster versions, but this one is easier to understand.

```
      DIMENSION IS(100,802),IEX(0:4)
C     2D ISING MODEL, FORTRAN 77 FOR IBM 32-BIT 8-SPIN-PER WORD-CODING
      DATA T,LL,MAX,ISEED/100,4.0,10,1/,MSK/Z10000000/
      L=8*LL
      PRINT *, T,L,MAX,ISEED
      IBM=2*ISEED-1
      T=T/0.440687
      DO 1 I=2,L+1
      DO 1 II=1,LL
1     IS(II,I)=0
      DO 2 I=0,4
      EX=EXP((4*I-8)/T)
2     IEX(I)=2147483648.0*(2.0*EX/(1.0+EX)-1)
      DO 6 ITIME=1,MAX
      DO 7 II=1,LL
      IS(II,  1)=IS(II,L+1)
7     IS(II,L+2)=IS(II,2)
      IBM=IBM*16807
      DO 4 I=2,L+1
      DO 4 II=1,LL
      ICI=IS(I1,I)
      IF(II.EQ.1 ) GOTO 10
      IF(II.EQ.LL) GOTO 11
      IEN=IEOR(IS(LL-1,I),ICI)+IEOR(      IS(II+1,I),ICI)
      GOTO 12
10    IEN=IEOR(IS(2   ,I),ICI)+IEOR(ISHFT(IS(LL,I),-4),ICI)
      GOTO 12
11    IEN=IEOR(IS(LLM1,I),ICI)+IEOR(ISHFT(IS(1 ,I), 4),ICI)
12    IEN=IEOR(IS(II,I-1),ICI)+IEOR(IS(II,I+1),ICI)+IEN
      ICH=0
      DO 3 IB=1,8
      ICH=ISHFT(ICH,-4)
      IBM=IBM*65539
      IF(IBM.LE.IEX(IAND(IEN,7))) ICH=IOR(ICH,MSK)
3     IEN=ISHFT(IEN,-4)
4     IS(II,I)=IEOR(ICI,ICH)
      M=0
      DO 5 I=2,L+1
      DO 5 II=1,LL
      ICI=IS(II,I)
      DO 5 IB=1,8
      M=M+IAND(ICI,1)
5     ICI=ISHFT(ICI,-4)
6     PRINT *,ITIME, M
      STOP
      END
```

3. REDUCE for Beginners

Six Lectures on the Application of Computer-Algebra (CA)

by

Volker Winkelmann[1,2] and Friedrich W. Hehl[2]

University of Cologne, Computer Center[1] and Institute of Theoretical Physics[2]
D-5000 Köln 41, W.Germany

Introduction

If you calculate on a computer by means of "letters" rather than with numbers, say you want to expand $(a + 27b^3 - 4c)^5$ or to integrate $\int 5x^2 \, sin^3 x \, dx$, then you are applying "computer algebra" (CA). For that purpose you need:

- access to a computer, that is to a PC (personal computer), a minicomputer, or a mainframe;

- a CA–system, like Anthony Hearn's Reduce 3.3, which should be installed on the computer under consideration; moreover, you want

- a user's manual, which you would get together with Reduce 3.3, say, if you purchased this CA–system.

And last but not least, you should have an introduction on how to use the CA-system.

These notes fulfill this purpose. They grew out of five lectures on Reduce, which we gave during two different terms at the University of Cologne to about 30 first to third year students of physics, mathematics, chemistry, and biology. The students were real beginners in CA. They could not necessarily handle a computer. The lectures were given in the computer laboratory of our department, with each student sitting in front of an intelligent terminal that could run Reduce 3.3 in its dialog version and which had, in addition, an editor for writing programs, if necessary.

Usually we first gave some extended explanations in the form of a lecture, with pauses for the students to call Reduce on their PC and to type in certain simple commands. Then we described some problems and their solutions, before (as part of the session) the students were assigned to solve a similar problem on their own, or together with their neighbors. Apart from ourselves, two teaching assistants were available to help the students. Afterwards one or two students presented their solutions. In this way, each lecture extended to about 4 to 5 hours of active work interrupted by our instruction.

Homework was distributed after each lecture, with about 5 examples to be solved within the intervening week. Overall, the course was quite fun; and the students, after five lectures (the sixth was added later), were able to progress alone with the help of the Reduce manual.

It was our policy to take exercises from ordinary mathematics or physics texts and not to tailor the problems so as to fit the computer or the CA-system. Hence, sometimes we solved problems with Reduce which one could also program in Basic or, attending the Stauffer or Zabolitzky part of our joint lecture course, even in Fortran. This was not the rule, however. Typically we have solved problems in Reduce which cannot be attacked in a straightforward way by means of Basic, Fortran, or Pascal.

These six lectures suppose that you have access to a computer running Reduce 3.3 (or an older version of it, in which case a few of the commands to be described may not be available). You can then use the lectures as a self–teaching course by carrying out the instructions given and solving the problems posed.

Reduce is one of the most widely distributed CA–systems. It already runs on a PC,[1] as well as on larger computers. There are other CA–systems, like MACSYMA, MAPLE, MATHEMATICA, μ–MATH, SAC–2, SCHOONSCHIP, SCRATCHPAD II and SMP, to name a few of the important systems.

For the user, the different CA-systems, with exception of Schoonschip and SAC–2, look very much the same. If you know how to use one system, then, with the help of the corresponding manual, you should be able to handle the other systems, too. Macsyma was originally developed at the MIT (Massachusetts Institute of Technology) and is, like Reduce, written in Lisp and can run, for example, on Symbolics computers and VAXes. Maple, developed at the University of Waterloo and written in C, is available on many UNIX-Systems and on VAXes, for example. The system Mathematica is brand new. Besides CA and numerics, it offers many graphic options. It was written in C and runs, for example, on the Apple Macintosh II and on Sun workstations. The small CA–system μ–Math runs on IBM compatible PC's, for instance. Schoonschip is an old system mainly for special use in high–energy physics. It was originally developed on a CDC computer. The Lisp–based Scratchpad II is a fairly recent development by IBM, and its data structure seems to be more flexible than those of the older systems.

We would like to thank Jürgen Altmann, Thomas Pfenning, and Andreas Strotmann for help in solving the exercises and in handling the computer hardware and software. We also appreciate very much useful suggestions by Drs. Rüdiger Esser (Jülich), Anthony Hearn (Santa Monica), Stan Kameny (Van Nuys), Dermott McCrea (Dublin), Eckehard Mielke (Cologne), Eberhard Schrüfer (St.Augustin), and by Thomas Wolf (Jena). We thank the Computer Center of our University for support.

---

[1] One cheap way to run Reduce on a personal computer, at least here in Germany, is to buy an Atari 1040ST which, including monitor and printer, costs as little as US$1000. Having an additional hard disc (for about $600) is convenient and to be recommended, though not indispensable. You can purchase Atari-Reduce for $500, see appendix A.1.

Lecture 1

"Computer algebra is that part of computer science which designs, analyzes, implements and applies algebraic algorithms." [2]

1.1 A first interactive Reduce session

Suppose you have a mathematical problem, namely to compute the value of

$$f = \lim_{x \to 0} \frac{x^3 \sin x}{(1 - \cos x)^2} \,, \tag{1.1}$$

that is, $f = \lim_{x \to 0} \frac{n}{d}$ with the numerator $n = x^3 \sin x$ and the denominator $d = (1 - \cos x)^2$. By substitution you find the undetermined value $\frac{0}{0}$. You may recall l'Hospital's rule and calculate $f = \lim_{x \to 0} \frac{n'}{d'}$, where a prime denotes derivation with respect to x. For (1.1), this yields $\frac{0}{0}$ again, so you have to compute $f = \lim_{x \to 0} \frac{n''}{d''}$ etc.; eventually you may get a well-determined f.

With Fortran, championed in Stauffer's and Zabolitzky's lectures, you would probably have a hard time if you tried to automate the "l'Hospital algorithm" on a computer. This is where computer–algebra (CA) steps in (in our lecture the CA-system Reduce). Here you can define n and n' as follows:

$$\texttt{N:=X**3*SIN(X);} \tag{1.2}$$

$$\texttt{NPRIME:=DF(N,X);} \tag{1.3}$$

First the value of $x^3 \sin x$ is assigned to the variable n. Observe that you must not leave out the multiplication sign *, nor forget a semicolon in order to terminate a command. Afterwards the derivative of the value of n (here $x^3 \sin x$) with respect to x is evaluated and then assigned to the newly defined variable $nprime$. Hence a CA–system is able to calculate derivatives, in spite of what its name may suggest. Therefore some people prefer to speak of "symbolic formula manipulation".

You can use Reduce in its dialog (interactive) version or in its batch version. In order to learn how Reduce works, you want to type in a command, wait for the answer of the machine, type in the next command – possibly correcting the first one – wait for the answer of the machine, and so forth. In contrast to this dialog version, you can submit to the batch version of Reduce well–tested programs consisting of many commands and requiring long execution times, say in the order of hours. But as beginners you may start the interactive Reduce by simply typing[3]

---

[2] This is the definition of R.Loos in the introduction of the monograph on "Computer Algebra" by B. Buchberger et al..

[3] In Atari–Reduce we click the lisp.ttp program and type in image=*name*, where *name* denotes the folder containing the Reduce files.

REDUCE

on your keyboard, or a similar call depending on your local implementation of Reduce. You need roughly 1 Mbyte of computer memory [4] in order to solve non–trivial problems with Reduce. It doesn't hurt, however, to have, for more complicated problems, a few more Mbyte available. The system should answer

```
REDUCE 3.3...

1:
```

Now you should type in (1.2) and hit the return key – it must always be hit in order to complete an input line. Subsequently type

```
D:=(1-COS(X))**2;
F:=DF(N,X)/DF(D,X);
X:=0;
F;
```

At this very moment Reduce will print

```
***** ZERO DENOMINATOR
```

that is, the evaluation of F has led to an error – error messages are always preceded by five stars – because the denominator of F has turned out to be zero. Don't worry, continue typing

```
CLEAR X;
F:=DF(N,X,2)/DF(D,X,2);
X:=0;
F;
```

and, after reiterating this process two more times, you will find on your display, in letting the computer evaluate F:=DF(N,X,4)/DF(D,X,4); , the limiting value as 4. To quit Reduce simply type in

```
BYE;
```

Later we will come back to this example. In order to store the information in a file, rather than directly typing it into Reduce, you can write the entire session in a small file with the help of your favorite editor (on the Atari with 1st Word Plus, for example, after you have switched off the word processor mode). It would read like

```
% file lhospit.rei
N:=X**3*SIN(X);
D:=(1-COS(X))**2;
```

---

[4] A bit measures a yes–no alternative, and 8 bit are called 1 byte. One million byte (more exactly 1024×1024 byte) are 1 Megabyte = 1 Mbyte.

```
F:=DF(N,X)/DF(D,X);

X:=0;

F;

CLEAR X;

F:=DF(N,X,2)/DF(D,X,2);

X:=0;

F;

CLEAR X;

F:=DF(N,X,3)/DF(D,X,3);

X:=0;

F;

CLEAR X;

F:=DF(N,X,4)/DF(D,X,4);

X:=0;

F;

CLEAR X;

END;
```

Notice that a Reduce input file must always be terminated with the command END;
. We named the file LHOSPIT.REI , the extension REI indicating a Reduce input file.
The part of a line after a percent sign % is considered by Reduce as a comment (alter-
natively, if the comment is longer than a line, one could use the command COMMENT
... ; where everything between COMMENT and ; is understood as a comment). Call
Reduce again. You can read in the file by the command

```
    IN LHOSPIT.REI;
```

or by IN "LHOSPIT.REI"; depending on your local Reduce system. After the first
three F; commands and the error messages ***** ZERO DENOMINATOR, the system
always asks: CONT? (Y or N). If you want to continue and to find the limiting value,
type y(es).

Exercise : Compute, according to the algorithm given, the value of

$$\lim_{x \to 0} \frac{e^{ax} - e^{bx}}{log(1 + x)} .$$

1.2 What can CA do for you?

From the Reduce manual we see that Reduce, among others, possesses the following features:

- Expansion and ordering of polynomials and rational functions, factorization of polynomials;

- simplification of expressions, execution of substitutions;

- differentiation and integration;

- calculations with matrices;

- precise integer and approximate floating point arithmetics;

- handling of built–in and user–defined functions;

- solving systems of linear equations;

- solving nonlinear algebraic equations;

- calculations in terms of exterior differential forms (Cartan calculus, useful in general relativity);

- writing Fortran programs (after having done some analytical calculations beforehand, for example);

- writing procedures for repeated use of commands;

- a high–energy physics package with Dirac–matrices for evaluating Feynman diagrams (that is how Reduce got started by A.C. Hearn); and

- determination of Lie symmetries of partial differential equations.

To give you a feel for the type of Reduce commands available, a small Reduce session of mostly unrelated commands follows:

```
% to get an impression of how Reduce works:
(X+Y)**2;
(X+Y)**17;

A:=(X+Y)**2;
B:=(U+Z)**2;
C:=A*B;
ON GCD;             % greatest common divisor is "on"
OFF EXP;            % expansion is "off", conventionally it is "on"
C;
DF(C,X);
```

```
DF(C,Z,3);

D:=DF((SIN X)**9,X);
FOR ALL X,Y LET SIN(X)*COS(Y)=(SIN(X-Y)+SIN(X+Y))/2;   % rule for
D;                                                      % sin*cos


FOR L:=1:50 SUM L;        % we need a FOR loop for what little
FOR L:=1:100 PRODUCT L;     % Gauss solved in elementary school


INT((SIN X)**9,X);        % integrating


MATRIX M(3,3);
M:=MAT((1,2,3),
       (4,5,6),
       (5,7,8));
DET M;                    % determinant of matrix M
1/M;                      % the inverse of matrix M


SOLVE(X**3-3*X**2-61*X+63,X);        % the solve package:
                                     % determine the zeroes


PROCEDURE FACTORIAL (K); % define your own procedure
    FOR L:=1:K PRODUCT L;


FACTORIAL(16);           % calculate 16!


OPERATOR LOG10;          % define your own function ("operator")
LET LOG10(10)=1;         % declare one of its math. properties
LOG10(10)*LOG10(20);     % does Reduce understand?
BYE;
```

So much for the small example session. Those of you who know Fortran or Pascal will discover that Fortran, Pascal and Reduce inputs are reminiscent of each other.

Reduce, like all programming languages, is built up from some basic elements, here from numbers, variables, operators, and so on. Out of these we are going to construct Reduce statements and expressions. For the rest of this lecture, we will turn to some of the basic elements – the rest of these will be treated in lecture 2.

1.3 The Reduce character set

This set is threefold. First of all, we have

- the 26 letters of the Latin alphabet, A,B,C...X,Y,Z. Most Reduce systems permit lower and upper case letters but don't distinguish between them, i.e., H and h have the same meaning for Reduce. Furthermore, we have

- the ten decimal digits 0 through 9. The letters and the digits are collectively called alphanumeric characters. Finally, there are

- the special characters

  + plus

  - minus

  * times

  / divided by

  = equals

  < less than

  > greater than

  (left parenthesis

) right parenthesis

  { left curly bracket

  } right curly bracket

  $ dollar sign, terminates a command with no printing of the result

  ; semicolon, terminates a command with printing of the result

  : colon, appears in loops and assignment statements, and with labels

  ! exclamation mark, represents the escape–character, see Sect.1.5

  " double quotes, mark the beginning and the end of a string

  % percent, preceeds a comment of no more then one line

  ' quote, a Lisp function not needed here

  . period or dot, denotes a special list operation, appears in floating point numbers and in the high–energy package

  , comma, used as a separator in certain commands

  | _ ^ @ # are used in the exterior calculus package of Reduce, see Sect.6.2

Incidentally, in Reduce some combinations of two special characters represent a single operator. Accordingly, ** means to the power of, <= less than or equal to, >= greater than or equal to, << begins and >> ends a group statement, and := represents the assignment operator, to name the most important examples.

1.4 Integers, rational and real numbers

Reduce knows several types of numbers:

- Integers like 1987, -273, +20. The remarkable thing in Reduce is that the integers are not limited in length[5] . Reduce is an ideal tool for accurately handling big integers. In practice, the length is, however, limited by the computer memory and the computer time available to you and also, of course, by your patience.

- Rational numbers as quotients of two integers like 2/3, -1977777/2222, +5/11.

- Real or floating–point numbers with a decimal point: 0.34, -456.7898E-2, 0.00478E3. The second and the third number are representations of $-456.7898 \times 10^{-2} = -4.567898$ and $0.00478 \times 10^3 = 4.78$, respectively. Observe that the decimal point must always be preceded or followed by a digit, that is, 0.5 is allowed, .5 and 2. are not.

- Complex numbers such as 5-I*8/9, - 68+48*I, with I as imaginary unit.

Type into your terminal

        5**65 * 2**102;

and, after some time, you will see what a real big number looks like. Integers and real numbers cannot be used in parallel[6] .

1.5 Variables named by identifiers

In CA we not only want to compute with numbers, but also are interested in evaluating algebraic expressions, series, integrals, and so on. Therefore we need variables.

In Reduce the so–called identifiers consist of one or more alphanumeric characters, where the first one must be alphabetic. Other characters can be used (even as first character) provided that each instance is preceded by the escape–character ! (exclamation mark). No unescaped blank (empty space) may appear within an identifier, and an identifier may not be extended over a line. Allowed identifiers are, for instance:

    V COLUMBUS ENERGY!-MOMENTUM !2OLD !7!-UP R2D2 C3PO !'T! HOOFT

Such identifiers can be used to name variables in Reduce, amongst other things. Identifiers can also name labels (which mark positions in compound statements), arrays, operators, procedures, etc..

---

[5] Actually, this is a property of the underlying Lisp system.

[6] If you turn on the float "switch" by typing ON FLOAT; only floating point numbers are allowed. You may come back to the integer arithmetics by the command OFF FLOAT; (see Sect.6.3).

We have a wide choice of variable names, but some restrictions do exist:

PI is the constant 3.14159263535... . Usually it is just a placeholder for π. But if you turn on the switches ON NUMVAL, FLOAT; , its numerical value as a floating point number is substituted by the system.

E is the Euler number, the base of the natural logarithm. Note: LOG(E) $\equiv$ 1. Its numerical value you get by means of ON NUMVAL, FLOAT; E;

I is, as we already mentioned, the imaginary unit, that is, the square root of -1, or I**2 $\equiv$ -1.

Finally we have the truth values of a boolean expression as reserved variables, namely

T which means "true" or "yes" and

NIL which means "false" or "no".

In fact, there are some more reserved words, a list of which you find in Appendix A of the Reduce manual.

1.6 A Reduce program, a follow–up of commands

A command is nothing more than a statement terminated by a semicolon or a dollar sign. These signs signal to Reduce that it should evaluate the preceding statement. The command

```
N:=DF(X**3*SIN(X),X);
```

means: Evaluate the statement N:=DF(X**3*SIN(X),X) , namely compute the derivative of the expression $x^3 \sin x$ with respect to x, and assign it to the variable n.

Statements are either expressions (to be described later in detail), or more complex control structures as exemplified by

```
A:=B
IF A=B THEN WRITE "EQUAL"
C:=K*(G:=9**7)
```

Also purely symbolic operators, which in Reduce provide specific actions, should be considered as statements:

```
ON DIV
OPERATOR RIEMANN
```

We met such statements in our sample session. ON DIV turns the division switch on. It forces common factors of rational functions to be divided out. RIEMANN is declared to be an operator, which represents a mathematical function.

As a rule, which is taken over from the underlying Lisp language, each statement has a value attributed to it (the more educated student may want to say "each statement evaluates to a value"). Therefore several statements can be combined, by means of operators like `+`, `-`, `*`, `/`, `**`, etc., to form a new statement.

The value of the statement `N:=DF(X**3*SIN(X),X)` is of interest to us. However, we do not worry what `ON DIV` evaluates to. The side effect of the `ON DIV`–statement, that is, the dividing out of factors, is important for us. The *value* of this statement is irrelevant in this context.

If the terminator after a statement is a semicolon, the value of the statement is usually printed out. If, however, we wish to suppress the result, we use the dollar sign. We shall come back to the discussion of statements later.

1.7 Assign a temporary result to a variable

In all programming languages it is important to save intermediate results for some length of time. For this purpose Reduce provides the *assignment statement*

$$expression_1 \; := \; expression_2$$

(remember that the semicolon is part of a command, but not part of a statement). Often $expression_1$ is just a variable, as in the examples

```
A:=(G+H)**3;
D:=(1-SIN(X))**2;
F:=A/DF(D,X,2);
X:=0;
F:=F;
```

The assignment of values to variables (or expressions) can be understood as follows: Apply the assignment operator `:=` to the expressions $expression_1$ and $expression_2$. In the first line, the right–hand–side `(G+H)**3` will be evaluated and assigned to the (unevaluated!) left–hand–side `A`. The value of the whole statement – and each statement has a value – is the value of the right hand side, here the value of `(G+H)**3`. Accordingly, our statement may be used within a more complex expression

```
A;
SIN(A:=D);
A;
```

where the value of `D` is assigned to `A` and, subsequently, the value of `A` is passed on as an argument to the mathematical operator `SIN`.

Example: Prove by induction that

$$1^4 + 2^4 + 3^4 + \ldots + n^4 \equiv \sum_{k=1}^{n} k^4 = \frac{n^5}{5} + \frac{n^4}{2} + \frac{n^3}{3} - \frac{n}{30}.$$

```
% 1**4 + 2**4 + 3**4 + 4**4 +...+ N**4          (x)


S:=N**5/5+N**4/2+N**3/3-N/30; % gen. formula (y) for series (x)


  N:=1;                         % (y) is correct for N=1,
  S;                            % since S --> 1, see (x)


  N:=K;                         % (y) is assumed valid for N=K
  SK:=S;                        % SK --> analogous to (y)


  N:=K+1;                       % in (y) we put N=K+1
  SKPLUS1:=S;                   % then we compute SKPLUS1 -->...


  SKPLUS1-SK-(K+1)**4;          % the difference of the two series
                                % must be (K+1)**4, see (x)
```

1.8 Homework

- Prove by induction that

$$\sum_{k=2}^{n} \frac{1}{(k-1)k} = \frac{n-1}{n}$$

and

$$\sum_{k=1}^{n} \frac{1}{k(k+1)(k+2)} = \frac{n(n+3)}{4(n+1)(n+2)}.$$

- Compute the zeroes of the the square polynomial

$$ax^2 + bx + c = 0.$$

The Reduce operator for the positive square root is SQRT, which means that the expression SQRT(X**2+2*X+1) evaluates to X+1. Substitute the following values for the coefficients (a, b, c): $(1, 1, 1)$, $(1, 1, -3)$, $(7, 1, -3)$, $(7, -5, -3)$, $(7, -5, 3)$. (Hint: Use the general solution $x_{1,2} = \left(-b \pm \sqrt{b^2 - 4ac}\right)/2a$.)

- Remark: Now that you are doing your first homework, it is decisive to keep track of the CPU–time which your computer needs for the execution of a certain Reduce program. In order to give you a hint of the order of magnitude, we run the same Reduce program *muster.exc*, which is described in *Schrüfer et al.*, on different machines. We and some of our colleagues found the following times: Cray X–MP 2400 (19 s), Amdahl 5860 (42 s), IBM 3081 (1 min 6 s), CDC Cyber 962 (1 min 32 s), Sun 3/260 (4 min), Atari Mega ST4 (42 min), CDC Cyber 180-830 (61 min 23 s)[7] . Of course, we quote these times with all due reservation, since they are implementation dependent, but it may give you an idea about the performance of your computer.

---

[7] The Cyber 962 run under the operating system NOS/VE with PSL (portable standard LISP), whereas the 180-830 used NOS/BE and UTLISP, respectively.

Lecture 2

In lecture 1 we demonstrated that Reduce programs are just a sequence of single commands. A command itself consists of a statement supplemented by a terminator, a semicolon if you want the value to be printed, otherwise a dollar sign. A statement may be composed of some "control structures" which, again, involve statements or expressions.

Since we intend to manipulate mathematical formulae, it is important for us to know how to construct Reduce expressions, because they can stand for what we usually call formulae. The image of a mathematical function is, in Reduce, an operator. An operator has a name[8] and it acts in a prescribed way on its arguments. These arguments in turn are Reduce expressions (see Sect.2.2).

2.1 Built-in operators

In lecture 1 we have already used, for example, the arithmetic operators + (plus) and * (times) in order to construct and combine expressions like $(x + y)^2$ or $x^3 \sin x$, which in Reduce read as (X+Y)**2 and X**3*SIN X, respectively. Here we have the + as an infix operator, that is, it is positioned in between its arguments, whereas SIN is a prefix operator, because it stands in front of its argument. In fact all built-in operators in Reduce belong to one of these types.

Let us give some more examples of *infix* operators (the blanks between the characters are optional, they only serve to improve the readability of an expression):

```
(U + V) * (Y - X) / 8
(A > B) AND (C < D)
```

The infix operators which are built into the standard system are

```
:=   +   -   *   /   **   =   NEQ   >=   >   <=   <   AND   OR   NOT
```

where ** means "to the power of" and NEQ "not equal". Obviously, the assignment operator :=, mentioned in lecture 1, is also of the infix type, since it assigns the value of the expression on its right–hand–side (its second argument) to the identifier on its left–hand–side (its first argument). The logical and relational operators

```
=   NEQ   >=   >   <=   <   AND   OR   NOT
```

are used to build boolean expressions, that is those which have only the truth values T (true) or NIL (false). They are only allowed within IF, WHILE, REPEAT, and LET statements. The operators >= > <= < can only compare expressions that evaluate to numbers, not arbitrary expressions such as polynomials.

---

[8] This name is either an identifier or composed of one or more special characters.

Prefix operators occur to the left of their arguments. The arguments are enclosed by parentheses and separated by commas:

```
COS (X)
INT(COS(X),X)
FACTORIAL(8)
```

Note that the parentheses can be omitted if the operator is unary (acts only on one argument):

```
COS(X)      may be written as  COS X (with a blank required for separartion)
COS(SIN(X)) may be written as  COS SIN X
```

The unary prefix operators, like SIN, COS, or LOG, have a precedence higher than any infix operator. This means that Reduce always interprets COS A*B as (COS(A))*B . Hence if unsure, always use parentheses in order to avoid unexpected results.

The following mathematical functions are built-in as prefix operators:

```
SIN,   COS,   TAN,    COT,    ASIN,   ACOS,   ATAN,
SINH,  COSH,  TANH,   ASINH,  ACOSH,  ATANH,  SQRT,
EXP,   LOG,   DILOG,  ERF,    EXPINT, ABS.
```

LOG is the natural logarithm (with the Euler number E as base), DILOG is Euler's dilogarithm $dilog(z) = -\int_0^z \frac{log(1-\zeta)}{\zeta} d\zeta$, ERF the Gaussian error function $erf(x) = \frac{2}{\sqrt{\pi}} \int_0^x e^{-t^2} dt$, EXPINT the exponential–integral function $expint(x) = \int_{-\infty}^x \frac{e^t}{t} dt$, and ABS the absolute–value function.

In addition to these built-in operators, the Reduce user may want to define her or his own operators by calling the command OPERATOR. More details about user-defined operators will be given later.

All operators may

- have values assigned to, as in

```
LOG(U):=12;
COS(2*K*PI):=1;
```

- have properties declared for some collections of arguments (for example, the value of SIN($integer$*PI) is always 0),

- be fully defined, either by the user, or by Reduce, as is the case for the operator DF for differentiation.

2.2 Manipulating Reduce expressions amounts to manipulating formulae

Since we already know which variables and operators are allowed, we are able to construct Reduce expressions combining variables and operators in such a way that they represent our mathematical formulae. Reduce distinguishes between three kinds of expressions: Integer, scalar, and boolean.

Integer expressions evaluate to whole numbers, for example

```
2
9-6
5**7+9*(6-J)*(K+H)
```

if J,K,H evaluate to integers.

Scalar expressions consist of (syntactically correct) sequences of numbers, variables, operators, left and right parentheses, and commas and are the usual representation of mathematical expressions in Reduce:

```
SIN(8*Y**4)+H(U)-(A+B)**7
DF(U,X,8)*PI
B(Y)+FACTORIAL(9)
A
```

The minimal scalar expressions which are known to Reduce are variables or numbers. The following rules are applied on evaluation of scalar expressions :

- Variables and operators with a list of arguments have the algebraic value they were last assigned or, if never assigned, stand for themselves.

- Nevertheless, some special expressions, such as elements of arrays (indexed variables), initially have the value 0.

- Procedures of expressions are evaluated with the values of their actual parameters used in the procedure call.

- The algebraic evaluation of expressions (also called simplification) is controlled by so-called switches which may be turned on or off by the Reduce user.

- In any case the standard rules of algebra apply. Parentheses are allowed. Expressions may be combined with legal operators to build new expressions. Those new expressions take on the new value built from the values of the subexpressions via the operators and taking into account the control switches.

Examples:

```
A*B;
POL;                        % still not assigned
POL:=(A+B)**3;              % now assigned
```

```
POL;
ON GCD;                         % greatest common divisor switch on
OFF EXP;                        % expansion switch off
POL;
F:=G*M*M/R**2;
ON DIV;                         % division switch on
F;
OFF GCD, DIV;  ON EXP;          % switches reset
```

Boolean expressions use the well–known boolean algebra and have truth values T for true and NIL for false. For handling of boolean expressions we have already mentioned the boolean infix operators. In addition, some prefix operators with boolean values will be introduced later. Boolean expressions are only allowed within IF, WHILE, or REPEAT statements. Examples of typical boolean expressions are

```
J NEQ 2
A=B AND (D OR G)
(A+7) > 18                      % if A evaluates to an integer
```

If you want to display the truth value of a boolean expression use the IF-statement (see Sect.3.1) as in the following example:

```
IF  2**28 <  10**7 THEN WRITE "less" ELSE WRITE "greater";
```

Several operators in Reduce, such as SOLVE or COEFF, usually need to return more than one value on evaluation. Therefore these values are returned as a list. A list in Reduce is an object consisting of elements surrounded by (curly) brackets and separated by commas. The elements themselves can be expressions or again lists. Examples of lists of expressions are

```
{EL1,EL2,EL3,EL4}
{A*(B+C)**4,{NOTHING},{Y,N,G,Q}}
```

Of course it is necessary to have simple operators in order to manipulate lists or to get hold of single elements of a list. These operators will be described in Sect.4.1.

2.3 The process of evaluation in Reduce

For writing Reduce programs, it is important to understand the evaluation process. After a terminator $ or ; has been sent to the computer, the whole command is evaluated. Each expression is evaluated from left to right, and the values obtained are combined with the operators specified. Sub–statements or sub–expressions existing within another expressions, like in

```
A:=SIN(G:=(X+7)**6);
COS(N:=2)*DF(X**10,X,N);
```

are always evaluated first. In the first case the value of (X+7)**6 is assigned to G, and then SIN((X+7)**6) is assigned to A. Note that the value of a whole assignment statement is always the value of its right–hand–side. In the second case Reduce assigns 2 to N, then computes DF(X**10,X,2), and last returns 90*X**8*COS(2) as the value of the whole statement. Note that this example represents bad programming style, which should be avoided.

One exception to the process of evaluation exists for the assignment operator := . Usually, the arguments of an operator are evaluated before the operator is applied to its arguments. In an assignment statement, the left side of the assignment operator is *not* evaluated. Hence

```
A:=B;
A:=C;
A;
```

will not assign C to B, but rather C to A.

The process of evaluation in an assignment statement can be studied in the following examples:

```
G:=1;
A:=(G+H)**3;
A;
```

Now A has the value of (1+H)**3 rather than (G+H)**3.

Sometimes it is necessary to remove the assigned value from a variable or an expression. This can be achieved by using the operator CLEAR as in

```
G:=1;
A:=(G+H)**3;
A;
CLEAR G;
A;
CLEAR A;
A;
```

or by overwriting the old value with the help of a new assignment statement:

```
CLEAR A,B;
A:=(U+V)**2;
A:=A-V**2;
A;
B:=B+1;
B;
```

The evaluation of A; results in the value U*(U+2*V), since (U+V)**2 had been assigned to A, and A-V**2 (i.e., (U+V)**2-V**2) was reassigned to A. The assignment B:=B+1;

will, however, lead to difficulty: Since no value was previously assigned to B, the assignment replaces B *literally* with B+1 (whereas the previous A:=A-V**2 statement produces the *evaluation* A:=(U+V)**2-V**2). The last evaluation B; will lead to an error or will even hang up the system, because B+1 is assigned to B. As soon as B is evaluated, Reduce returns B+1, whereby B still has the value B+1, and so on. Therefore the evaluation process leads to an infinite loop. Hence we should avoid such recursions.

Let us now turn to some new Reduce statements.

2.4 Repeatedly doing something: Loops

It is often necessary to evaluate a statement several times with discrete increments or decrements in the value of one specific variable. Therefore in many programming languages a statement exists for building loops; in Reduce this is the FOR-statement. A simple example is the computation of the product $x(x+2)(x+4)(x+6)\ldots(x+24)$. In Reduce it may read

```
PROD := 1;
FOR L:=0 STEP 2 UNTIL 24 DO PROD:=PROD*(X+L);
PROD;
```

More generally, the format of the FOR–statement is as follows:

FOR *loop–variable*:=*start* STEP *increment* UNTIL *end* DO *statement*

For all possible numerical values in the range between and including *start* and *end* with stepsize *increment* every occurrence of *loop–variable* in *statement* is substituted by the current value and *statement* is evaluated. Incidentally, the FOR–statement itself evaluates to 0. If the increment is 1, the following abbreviation may be used:

FOR *loop–variable* := *start* : *end* DO *statement*

One example is the determination of $\sum_{l=1}^{13} l^4$:

```
QUATRO:=0;
FOR L:=1:13 DO QUATRO:=QUATRO+L**4;
QUATRO;
```

Incidentally, *loop–variable* is a local identifier. Accordingly, any legal identifier may be used as *loop–variable*, even I or E. However, in that case I and E must not be used in *statement* as imaginary unit or Euler number, respectively, since they would be always substituted by the current value of *loop–variable* .

Very often products and sums are computed in FOR-loops, for example in expansions, series, etc.. Therefore Reduce provides the additional possibility of computing the product or sum of the individual results of evaluating *statement* :

        FOR *loop-variable* := *start* STEP *increment* UNTIL *end* PRODUCT *statement*

and

        FOR *loop-variable* := *start* STEP *increment* UNTIL *end* SUM *statement*

In contrast to the DO-version, now the value of the whole FOR-statement is the PRODUCT or the SUM of all single values of *statement*. Hence the examples given above can be written in a simpler way:

```
PROD:=FOR L:=0 STEP 2 UNTIL 24 PRODUCT (X+L);
```

and

```
QUATRO:=FOR L:=1:13 SUM L**4;
```

Example: Compute the Taylor expansion for $e^x \approx 1 + \sum_{n=1}^{10} \frac{x^n}{n!}$ and evaluate the expansion at $x = 0.1$:

```
EX:=1 + FOR N:=1:10 SUM X0**N/(FOR L:=1:N PRODUCT L);
ON FLOAT;
X0:=0.1;
EX;
OFF FLOAT;
```

Often an operation is repeated until a certain condition is met. For this purpose the WHILE-statement is used:

        WHILE *boolean expression* DO *statement*

Here *boolean expression* controls the evaluation of the statement following DO. The condition is always checked *before* the action follows. WHILE repeats the statement until the condition is false, as in the following example:

Test after which n the $\sum_{j=1}^{n} j^4$ is greater than 10000:

```
J:=1;
SERIES:=0;
WHILE (SERIES:=SERIES + J**4) < 10000 DO J:=J+1;
J;
SERIES;
```

The sum is computed and compared, whereas the variable is counted in the statement following DO.

REPEAT is very much like WHILE, but it tests the condition *after* every evaluation of *statement*. Its format is

        REPEAT *statement* UNTIL *boolean expression*

The same example with a REPEAT–statement reads:

```
J:=0;
SERIES:=0;
REPEAT J:=J+1 UNTIL (SERIES:=SERIES + J**4) > 10000;
J;
SERIES;
```

2.5 Loops and lists

Within a FOR–statement it is also possible to collect all computed individual results in one list. This might be useful if later one wants to refer to a single result or to use it as an argument in operators or procedure calls:

FOR *loop-variable* := *start* STEP *increment* UNTIL *end* COLLECT *statement*

Compute, for example, $n!$ for $n = 1, ...13$:

```
DUMMY:=1;
FOR N:=1:13 COLLECT DUMMY:=DUMMY*N;
```

The value of a specific statement may be a list. Hence, if the single results of the evaluated statement in a FOR–loop are lists, we can join these lists to a single list by using the JOIN action:

FOR *loop-variable* := *start* STEP *increment* UNTIL *end* JOIN *statement*

Compare the following commands:

```
FOR N:=1:5 COLLECT {(X+1)**N}; %result: 1 list containing 5 lists
FOR N:=1:5 JOIN    {(X+1)**N}; %result: 1 list with 5 elements
```

Operators which have lists as arguments or evaluate to lists will be described later (see SOLVE, COEFF in Sects.4.3 and 4.4).

In the FOR–statements described above, the iteration was controlled by a loop variable. Instead of the incremental loop variable, the elements of a list can take its place. They are substituted successively into *statement*. Then we have a new form of the FOR–statement providing the same action to DO, PRODUCT, SUM, COLLECT, and JOIN:

FOR EACH *variable* IN *list* DO/SUM/PRODUCT/COLLECT/JOIN *statement*

In this form every occurence of *variable* in *statement* is replaced by the next element of *list*. Then *statement* is evaluated and the action desired takes place until all elements of *list* are processed.

Examples: Evaluate the polynomial $x^2 - 3x + 15$ at $x = 0, 1.5, 2.5, 10$, and put the values received into one list:

```
FOR EACH X IN {0,3/2,5/2,10} COLLECT X**2-3*X+15;
```

Compute the sum of 7!, 12!, 13!, 18!, 20!. We know how to compute factorials:

```
FOR L:=2:N PRODUCT L;                    % if N has an integer value
```

Hence it is easy to build the sum:

```
FOR EACH N IN {7,12,13,18,20} SUM (FOR L:=2:N PRODUCT L);
```

2.6 Multidimensional objects: Arrays

As we have seen, it is possible to program iterations or to repeat statements with FOR, WHILE, and REPEAT. Under these circumstances, very often variables with one or more indices are necessary in order to define vectors, tensors, or other "multidimensional objects". In Reduce such objects may be declared by an ARRAY–statement:

```
ARRAY VECT(10), MA(5,5), E605(60,5,9);
```

This declaration is similar to a Fortran dimension statement, but here the array indices range from 0 to the value declared. Thus, the array VECT has 11 and MA has 6×6 components. The array elements are referred to through their indices:

```
VECT(5):=X+Y-Z**3;
VECT(5);
```

The polynomial on the right–hand–side is assigned to the component number 5 of VECT and may be referred to by VECT(5). Initially, before any assignment, every element of an array has the value of 0. Hence it is very easy to setup series.

Exercises: Compute the so–called Fibonacci series a_n, $n = 1...20$, where $a_n = a_{n-1} + a_{n-2}$, $a_0 = 0$, $a_1 = 1$:

```
CLEAR A;                        % to avoid a possible conflict
ARRAY A(20);                    % with a previously defined A
A(1):=1;
FOR L:=2:20 DO A(L):=A(L-1)+A(L-2);
A(17);                          % 1597
```

(Observe that A(0) was zero after the ARRAY declaration.) Compute $I_n = \int_0^1 x^n e^x dx$, with $n = 1...10$ by using the recursion relation $I_n = e - nI_{n-1}$ with $I_0 = e - 1$, and save the results in an array:

```
ARRAY INTX(10);
INTX(0):=E-1;
FOR L:=1:10 DO INTX(L):=E-L*INTX(L-1);
```

Arrays can also be used to represent tensors. Let us, for example, compute (in a flat Minkowski spacetime in Cartesian coordinates) the covariant components of a vector x_i from its given contravariant components x^i. The metric reads $g_{ij} = diag(-1, 1, 1, 1)$, and we use the formula $x_i = \sum_{j=0}^{3} g_{ij} x^j$:

```
ARRAY GLL(3,3), XL(3), XH(3);
GLL(0,0):=-1; GLL(1,1):=1; GLL(2,2):=1; GLL(3,3):=1;
XH(0):=TAU; XH(1):=X; XH(2):=Y; XH(0):=Z;
FOR K:=0:3 DO XL(K):= FOR J:=0:3 SUM GLL(K,J)*XH(J);
```

Now the array XL (L for "low", H in XH for "high") contains the covariant components x_i of the vector. Of course, this example is somewhat trivial. But if we turn, say, to polar coordinates, Reduce may save a lot of work.

2.7 Homework

- Compute the characteristic polynomial of $\begin{pmatrix} a & 0 & 5 \\ 1 & 1 & 1 \\ -a & 0 & 0 \end{pmatrix}$.

- Compute the approximate value of the natural logarithm from its power series expansion up to 5th order:

$$ln\,(1+x) \approx \sum_{n=1}^{5} (-1)^{n+1} \frac{x^n}{n} \quad .$$

- Compute the integral $I_n = \int_0^1 x^n e^x \, dx$ by using the relation

$$I_n = e \sum_{m=0}^{n} (-1)^m \frac{n!}{(n-m)!} - (-1)^n n! \quad .$$

- Compute the product of two arbitrary 6×6 matrices and assign the result to a third matrix according to

$$c_{ij} = \sum_{k=1}^{6} a_{ik} b_{kj} \quad .$$

Lecture 3

In lecture 2 we learnt something about the evaluation process. Moreover, we studied statements, like the FOR–statement, which are often used. In this lecture, we will first concentrate on the conditional, the group, and the compound statements and then turn to a couple of useful operators, for example the differentiation and the integration operators.

3.1 The conditional statement

Very often the evaluation of a certain statement depends on a previously evaluated statement. Therefore it is necessary to have a conditional statement available which allows one to evaluate an expression or a statement under certain conditions or criteria. The conditional statement of Reduce is built according to the pattern

      IF *boolean expression* THEN *statement*₁

or

      IF *boolean expression* THEN *statement*₁ ELSE *statement*₂

The value of such an IF–statement depends on the value of *boolean expression*. If it is true, then the value of the whole IF–statement is the value of *statement*₁. If it is false, the value is 0 or, if ELSE is provided, the value of *statement*₂. Let us look at two examples:

```
A:=3;    B:=7;    C:=8;    D:=3;
IF A=D THEN C;
IF A = 0 AND B NEQ 0 THEN X0:=-C/B ELSE X0:=Y+C**2;
X0;
```

An IF–statement is just another statement. Therefore we may use an IF–statement within another, as, for example, in

```
ZERO:=  IF B = 0 AND A NEQ 0
        THEN SQRT(-C/A)
        ELSE IF B NEQ 0
             THEN SQRT(-C/B);
```

after the ELSE. In certain cases, as when an IF–statement is inserted following THEN, it may be necessary to enclose the statement in parentheses to avoid ambiguity, as in:

```
IF A=B THEN (IF B=0 THEN C:=B)
       ELSE C:=A;
```

Remember that an IF–statement returns a value which can be assigned to a variable, as in the last but one example, or which can be used in an expression:

```
SECRET:=(IF A=8 THEN 9 ELSE 10)*12; % note: no terminator appears
                                    % in the IF-statement
```

Exercise: Find a solution of the quadratic equation $ax^2 + bx + c = 0$ with arbitrary a, b, c. Test your program with $a = 0$, $b = 3$, $c = 6$ and $a = 9$, $b = 18$, $c = 9$:

```
CLEAR ERROR,ARBITRARY;
A:=0;   B:=3;   C:=6;
X1:=IF A=0
    THEN IF B=0                                % a=0
         THEN IF C NEQ 0                       % a=0,b=0
              THEN ERROR                       % a=0,b=0,c unequ.0
              ELSE ARBITRARY                   % a=0,b=0,c=0
         ELSE -C/B                             % a=0,b unequ.0
    ELSE  -B/(2*A)+SQRT(-(C/A)+(B/(2*A))**2);  % a unequ.0


A:=9;   B:=18;   C:=9;
X1:=IF A=0
      .
      .
      .
```

The IF–statement returns one solution of the equation, the value of the variable ERROR if $a, b = 0$ and $c \neq 0$, or the value of the variable ARBITRARY if all coefficients are zero.

3.2 Combining several statements I: The group statement

Very often, within FOR–, WHILE–, and REPEAT–statements, it is useful to evaluate more than one statement at the same time. Therefore in Reduce *several* statements may be combined into *one* new statement by means of the group or the compound statement. The group statement is of the form

$$\ll statement_1;\ statement_2;\ .\ .\ .\ statement_{n-1};\ statement_n \gg$$

The evaluation of such a group statement is performed by executing each of the statements one after another. Let us compute, for example, $\prod_{n=1}^{10} n$ and $\sum_{n=1}^{10} n$:

```
PROD:=1; S:=0;
FOR N:=1:10 DO <<S:=S+N; PROD:=PROD*N>>;
PROD;
S;
```

The group statement is to be understood as *one* new statement which has *one* value, namely the value of the last statement enclosed by $\ll \ldots \gg$, as in

```
A:=<<M:=(X+Y)**7;N:=(X-Y)**7;M*N>>;
```

Here (X+Y)**7 is assigned to M and (X-Y)**7 to N. The value of the last statement is the value of the group statement. The last statement M*N evaluates to (X**2-Y**2)**7, and this value is assigned to A.

The last statement in a group statement must *not* be followed by a terminator, because this causes the group statement to have the value 0. Hence the last example with a semicolon after M*N

```
A:=<<M:=(X+Y)**7;N:=(X-Y)**7;M*N  ;  >>;
```

assigns (X+Y)**7 to M, (X-Y)**7 to N, and 0 to A!

Exercise: Set up the antisymmetric arrays a and b with $a_{ij} = -a_{ji} = i \times j$ and $b_{ij} = -b_{ji} = i + j$, $i < j$:

```
CLEAR A,B;                        % they were used earlier
ARRAY A(3,3),B(3,3);
FOR L:=0:3 DO A(L,L):=B(L,L):=0;  % not really necessary, why?
FOR L:=1:3 DO FOR R:=0:(L-1) DO << A(L,R):=-(A(R,L):=L*R);
                                   B(L,R):=-(B(R,L):=L+R) >>;
```

3.3 Combining several statements II: The compound statement

We can combine several statements into one compound (or block) statement as follows:

```
BEGIN; statement₁; .    .    .    statementₙ; END;
```

Within a compound statement (in contrast to the group statement) we can introduce local variables by a SCALAR declaration, we can jump within the compound statement by means of a GOTO–statement to a label, we can RETURN a value as the value of the whole compound statement, or we can stop evaluation if a certain condition is met. Incidentally, the semicolon after *statementₙ* may be omitted - BEGIN ...END act like brackets.

Without all these conveniences, we can write the last example of Sect.3.2 alternatively as

```
ARRAY A(3,3),B(3,3);
FOR L:=0:3 DO A(L,L):=B(L,L):=0;
FOR L:=1:3 DO FOR R:=0:(L-1) DO
   BEGIN;
      A(L,R):=-(A(R,L):=L*R);
      B(L,R):=-(B(R,L):=L+R);
   END;
```

Since the SCALAR and the RETURN statement are missing, no local variables exist and the value of this new (compound) statement is 0.

In the previous example, no local variables were needed nor used. However, consider the following example:

```
CLEAR A;B;
A:=B:=9041987;
BEGIN SCALAR A,B;
    A:=(X+Y)**3;
    B:=(X-Y);
    C:=A/B;
END;
A;
B;
C;
```

The SCALAR declaration is used to declare the local variables A and B. Local means that the values of the variables are deleted as soon as the whole block is evaluated and there is no conflict with variables outside the block that happen to have the same name. The declaration must follow immediately the keyword BEGIN, and the variables mentioned in the SCALAR declaration initially have the value zero.

In the form described so far, the compound statement always has a value zero. However, the RETURN statement can change that:

$$BEGIN\ SCALAR\ variable_1, variable_2, \ldots variable_n;$$

$$statement_1; \ \ldots \ statement_n;\ RETURN\ expression;$$

END;

The value of the whole compound statement is now determined by the value of the RETURN statement. Using the previous example:

```
C:= BEGIN SCALAR A,B;
        A:=(X+Y)**3;
        B:=(X-Y);
        RETURN B*A
    END;
C;
```

It is also possible to place the RETURN statement earlier, but the RETURN always causes Reduce to leave the block and to skip all statements up to the END of the block. Therefore this is sensible only if a conditional statement controls the RETURN statement. Note that RETURN can only be used within a compound statement, it must not be used on the so-called toplevel of Reduce.

We can define jumps to labels within one compound statement by

label: *statement*

where jumps are initiated by the GOTO statement:

GOTO *label*

The example of computing 37! by means of a GOTO loop will make it clear:

```
N:=37;
BEGIN SCALAR M;
    M:=1;
  L: IF N=0 THEN RETURN M;          % even 0! can be computed
    M:=M*N;
    N:=N-1;
    GO TO L;
END;
```

3.4 Some elementary mathematical functions

In lecture 2 we mentioned built-in operators. Some of the more important built-in *prefix* operators will be described now. They are refered to by their name (operator's name) and they depend on one or more arguments which are enclosed in parentheses. Let us turn to MAX and MIN. They evaluate to the maximum or minimum of the numerical expressions given in their arguments:

```
MIN(3,5,6,3,1,8,9);       % evaluates to 1
A:=9;
MAX(8,A,7);               % evaluates to 9
```

The prefix operators which represent mathematical functions have already been listed in Sect 2.1. These operators are predefined for certain values such as for 0, 1, π etc. Since these operators carry only one argument, the parentheses may be omitted:

```
SIN(PI);                  % evaluates to 0
EXP(1);                   % evaluates to E
LOG 2;                    % evaluates to LOG(2)
(SIN X)**2+(COS X)**2;    % evaluates to (SIN X)**2+(COS X)**2
```

Not all well–known rules, such as the addition theorems for sine and cosine, are predefined. They may be imposed by the LET rules for operators, which we will describe in Sects.4.8 and 5.1.

3.5 Differentiation with DF

The operator DF can be used for partial differentation with respect to a variable according to the pattern

```
DF(expression,variable);
```

Simple examples are

```
DF(X**3+2/X,X);
```

```
DF((SIN(Z))**9,Z);
```

If you want to compute, however, the n-th derivative of *expression* with respect to *variable*, use

```
DF(expression,variable,n);
```

as in

```
DF(X**3+2/X,X,3);
DF((SIN(Z))**9,Z,6);
```

We can also successively determine the n_1st derivative of *expression* with respect to *variable*$_1$, then the n_2nd derivative of the expression calculated with respect to *variable*$_2$, and so on:

```
DF(expression, variable₁, n₁, variable₂, n₂...);
```

This is demonstrated in the examples

```
DF(X**6+2*Y**3*X**3+1,X,3,Y,2);
DF(SIN(X)*COS(Y)*LOG(Z),X,2,Y,2,Z,2);
```

What happens for DF(LOG(Y),R); ? The derivative vanishes if a variable does not appear in *expression*. Only operators which have the specified variable in their argument(s) will be differentiated. However, consider the last example. If you want to tell Reduce that actually Y depends on R, you can use the DEPEND statement:

```
DEPEND Y,R;
DF(LOG(Y),R);
```

Now the derivative no longer vanishes, and the chain rule is applied, if possible. The dependence can be removed with NODEPEND:

```
DF((LOG Y)**3,R);
NODEPEND Y,R;
DF((LOG Y)**3,R);
```

Exercise: For $y = x^n \log x$, verify the relation $xy' = x^n + ny$.

```
CLEAR X,Y,N;
Y:=X**N*LOG(X);
DF(Y,X)*X-(X**N+N*Y);
```

Since the last term evaluates to zero, the identity is proved.

3.6 Integration with INT

Now that our differentiation work can be executed by Reduce, naturally we want Reduce to do analytic integration, too. For this purpose Reduce offers the operator

    INT(*expression, variable*)

INT tries to integrate *expression* with respect to *variable* and returns, if successful, the indefinite integral. The arbitrary constant is suppressed. Examples are:

```
CLEAR X,Y;
INT(SIN X,X);          % evaluates to -COS(X)
INT(LOG Y,Y);          % evaluates to Y*(LOG(Y)-1)
INT(FCT(X)*X,X);       % evaluates to INT(FCT(X)*X,X),
                       % since FCT(X) is not yet specified
```

If INT cannot compute the integral, it will return a (sometimes simplified) expression involving one or more parts in the INT-form which could not be integrated. Nevertheless, sometimes Reduce does not find an integral, even if it can be represented in a closed form. Thus the usefulness of the integration package is somewhat limited.

The INT operator is part of a separate Reduce package and may not be implemented at all sites. Normally the integration package is loaded automatically if the INT operator is called. If not, try the command

    LOAD INT;

or LOAD "INT";. Otherwise ask your local software manager.

Reduce provides an additional package for indefinite integration of square roots, called ALGINT. If you want to integrate such functions, load this module:

```
LOAD ALGINT;
INT(1/SQRT(X**4+2*X**2),X);
```

Integrate, for example, $x^4 e^x$, e^{x^2}, $(2x^2 - x - 1)^{-1}$ with respect to x, and verify the results by subsequent differentiation:

```
F:=X**4*E**X;
INTF:=INT(F,X);
F-DF(INTF,X);
```

3.7 Substitution with SUB

Often one would like to make a local substitution for a sub–expression within an expression without changing any "global binding", that is without destroying previous assignments etc.. The SUB operator replaces every occurrence of $variable_i$ in *old expression* by $expression_i$:

SUB($variable_1 = expression_1, \ldots variable_n = expression_n, old\ expression$)

The value computed by SUB is the value of *old expression*, after every occurrence of $variable_1$ has been substituted by $expression_1$, $variable_2$ by $expression_2$, and so on. Some example are:

```
CLEAR A,B,X,Y,XO;
A:=(X+Y)**3;
B:=1+(X+XO)+(X+XO)**2/2+(X+XO)**3/6;
SUB(X=1,A);                 % evaluates to Y**3+3*Y**2+3*Y+1
SUB(XO=0,B);                % evaluates to X**3/6+X**2/2+X+1
SUB(X=1,Y=2,A);            % evaluates to 27
SUB(Y=1,X=Y-1,A);         % evaluates to Y**3
SUB(X=PI/2,DF(SIN X**9*X**3/(X+1)**5,X,6)); %builds the 6th
%derivative and computes the value of the funct. at X=PI/2.
```

The proof in Sect.1.7 of the sum rule for the series $1^4 + 2^4 + \ldots + n^4$ can now be made a bit more transparent:

```
S:=N**5/5+N**4/2+N**3/3-N/30;    % general formula for series
SUB(N=1,S);                       % S --> 1, i.e., valid for N=1
SUB(N=K+1,S)-SUB(N=K,S)-(K+1)**4; % must be 0, q.e.d.
```

3.8 Homework

- Given an arbitrary array $a = \begin{pmatrix} a_{00} & a_{01} & a_{02} \\ a_{10} & a_{11} & a_{12} \\ a_{20} & a_{21} & a_{22} \end{pmatrix}$, compute the symmetric part $a_{(ij)} = (a_{ij} + a_{ji})/2$ and the antisymmetric part $a_{[ij]} = (a_{ij} - a_{ji})/2$ and assign them to new arrays b_{ij} and c_{ij}

- Program the basic algorithm for the Taylor series of an arbitrary function $f(x)$ at $x = x_0$. Test your algorithm with the following functions:

$$e^x \text{ at } x_0 = 0$$

$$log(x) \text{ at } x_0 = 1$$

$$sin(x) \text{ at } x_0 = 0$$

$$sinh\left(3\ log(3 + x - x^2)\right) \text{ at } x_0 = 0$$

Verify for the first 5 terms:

$$e^{iz} = \cos z + i \sin z$$

$$\sin z = -i \sinh iz$$

$$\cos z = \cosh iz$$

(Hints: Use a variable FCT in order to represent the function $f(x)$. FCT itself should depend on an arbitrary variable X. Use FOR and SUB and expand at X0.)

- Compute the Euler number e up to 10 decimal places. Use ON FLOAT; in order to display the decimal form of the result.

- Evaluate the following integrals:

$$\int_0^1 x^n e^x dx \quad \text{for } n = 0 \ldots 10$$

$$\int_0^\pi \sin^5 x dx$$

$$\int_0^1 (a^n - x^m)^n dx \quad \text{for } m, n = 1, 2, 3, 4$$

- Verify for $z = \log(x^2 + y^2)$:

$$\left(\frac{\partial z}{\partial x}\right)^2 + \left(\frac{\partial z}{\partial y}\right)^2 = 4e^{-z} \quad .$$

(Hint: The identity $e^{\log x} \equiv x$ is not known to Reduce; use E**LOG(X**2+Y**2):= X**2+Y**2.)

Lecture 4

We will now continue with prefix operators provided by Reduce. Some of these operators, after evaluation, return more than one value. Therefore the values are put into a list, which is a set of elements enclosed by two curly brackets[9] . The elements may be expressions or again lists:

```
{EL1,EL2,EL3,EL4}
{A*(B+C)**4,{NOTHING},{Y,N,G,Q}}
```

Some operators even take lists as arguments. Hence it is necessary to have operators at one's disposal which extract single expressions out of a list or which can combine lists and the like.

4.1 Operators that act on lists

The operators FIRST, SECOND, and THIRD return the first, second, or third element of a list:

```
SECOND({A,B,C});                % evaluates to B
```

REST returns the list with its first member removed:

```
REST({A,B,C});                  % evaluates to {B,C}
```

Furthermore, one is able to APPEND one list to another one:

```
APPEND({A,B,C},{D,E});          % evaluates to {A,B,C,D,E}
```

REVERSE yields a list in which the elements appear in reverse order:

```
REVERSE({A,B,C,D});             % evaluates to {D,C,B,A}
```

The . operator (CONS or dot operator) inserts one expression at the front of a list. Finally, LENGTH determines the number of elements of a list:

```
A:={ALPHA,2*BETA,GAMMA/DELTA};
SECOND(A);                      % evaluates to 2*BETA
REST(A);                        % evaluates to {2*BETA,GAMMA/DELTA}
APPEND({1,2,3,{4}},REVERSE(A));    % evaluates to {1,2,3,{4},
                                %         GAMMA/DELTA,2*BETA,ALPHA}
(2*6) . REST(A);                % evaluates to
                                %         {12,2*BETA,GAMMA/DELTA}
LENGTH(A);                      % evaluates to 3
```

---

[9] Strictly speaking, the operator returns only one value - and the value is the list.

4.2 Right and left–hand–side of an equation

Generally mathematical equations like the one for a circle with radius r in cartesian coordinates

$$x^2 + y^2 = r^2$$

cannot be translated directly into Reduce. However, it is possible to have an equation of the form

$$expression_l = expression_r$$

as argument for some operators. The left or right–hand–side of such an equation may be extracted by the built-in operators LHS and RHS:

```
LHS(X**2+2*X=Y-3);        % evaluates to X**2+2*X
RHS(X**2+2*X=Y-3);        % evaluates to Y-3
```

Later some operators will be described which apply to lists and equations.

4.3 Solving (non-)linear equations

The SOLVE operator solves systems of both linear or single nonlinear algebraic equations. Its format is:

SOLVE($expression_1$, $variable_1$)

or

SOLVE($\{expression_1, \ldots expression_n\}, \{variable_1, \ldots variable_n\}$)

If SOLVE is called, it tries to solve $expression_1 = 0 \ldots expression_n = 0$ with respect to the unknowns $variable_1 \ldots variable_n$. SOLVE returns a list of solutions. If there is one unknown, each solution is an equation for the unknown. If a complete solution is found, the unknown appears on the left hand side of the equation. If SOLVE is not successful, the "solution" will be an equation for the unknown. Examples are:

```
SOLVE(LOG(SIN(X+3))**5-8,X);        % finding the zeroes of that
                                    %    function
SOLVE(1/(1+X**2) = Y, X);           % finding the inverse function
                                    %    of Y=1/(1+X**2)
SOLVE({CONST*X+Y=3,Y+2=0},{X,Y});   % finding the solution for X,Y
                                    %    of the linear system
```

We can extract from the solution list a solution for a particular variable by using the operators FIRST, SECOND, THIRD, REST and LHS, RHS:

```
SOLUTION:=SOLVE(X**2-1,X);
S1:=RHS(FIRST(SOLUTION));
S2:=RHS(SECOND(SOLUTION));
```

Several inverse functions are known to Reduce, those of LOG, SIN, COS, **, ACOS, ASIN, for example. For more information on the SOLVE operator, please consult Sect.7.7 of the Reduce manual.

Exercises:

- Find the local minima or maxima of $f(x) = 3x^3 - 7x + 1$:

    ```
    SOLVE(DF(3*X**3-7*X+1,X),X);
    ```

- Compute dy/dx from the equation $log(x^2 + y^2) = 2\,arctan(x/y)$:

    ```
    DEPEND Y,X;
    F:=LOG(X**2+Y**2)-2*ATAN(X/Y);
    SOLVE(DF(F,X),DF(Y,X));
    ```

- Given the equations

$$y_1 = 6x_1 + 2x_2 + 3x_3$$
$$y_2 = 4x_1 + 5x_2 - 2x_3$$
$$y_3 = 7x_1 + 2x_2 + 4x_3 \qquad ,$$

find the inverse equations:

```
L:=SOLVE( {6*X1+2*X2+3*X3=Y1,
           4*X1+5*X2-2*X3=Y2,
           7*X1+2*X2+4*X3=Y3}, {X1,X2,X3} );
L:=FIRST(L);
```

The SOLVE operator is part of a separate Reduce package. If it is not loaded automatically, try the command LOAD SOLVE;

4.4 Retrieving parts of polynomials and rational functions

The numerator and the denominator of a rational function are determined as follows:

> NUM *expression*   DEN *expression*

Examples are:

```
CLEAR A;
A:=B/C;
NUM A;              % evaluates to B
DEN A;              % evaluates to C
NUM (A**2);         % evaluates to B**2
DEN(100/6);         % evaluates to 3, since the argument is
                    %                         evaluated first!
NUM(B/4 +C/6)       % evaluates to 3*B + 2*C
```

Example: Evaluate the expression

$$\frac{(x+1)^2 \sin x}{x^3 + 13x^2 + 50x + 56}$$

at $x = -10$, -7, -4, -1; if a term is singular, then return the value infinite:

```
FCT:=(X+1)**2*SIN(X)/(X**3+13*X**2+50*X+56);
FOR EACH L IN {-10,-7,-4,-1} COLLECT
    IF SUB(X=L,DEN(FCT)) NEQ 0
        THEN SUB(X=L,FCT) ELSE INFINITE;
```

The coefficients of a polynomial in terms of a main *variable* may be determined by

COEFF (*polynomial*, *variable*)

A list containing the coefficients of *polynomial* with respect to *variable* is returned, ordered with the coefficients of the highest power at the rightmost position. The length of the list is equal to one more than the highest order of *variable* in *polynomial*:

```
COEFF(X**2+2*X*Y+Y**2,X);       %evaluates to {Y**2,2*Y,1}
```

Normally COEFF only works on expressions that do not have denominators dependent on *variable*. Nevertheless, it is possible to avoid the checking of the denominators when the switch RATARG is turned on: The numerator is processed by COEFF, and the result, as desired, is the list of these coefficients divided by the denominator:

```
A:=(5*X+1)**3/X;
COEFF(A,X);                % leads to an error
ON RATARG;
COEFF(A,X);                % evaluates to {1/X,15/X,75/X,125/X}
```

An operator exists, similar to COEFF, for determining a particular coefficient:

COEFFN (*polynomial*, *variable*, *n*)

It yields the coefficient of the *n*th power of *variable* in *polynomial*, as, for example, in

```
COEFFN((2*X+Y)**3,X,3);    % evaluates to 8
```

For additional commands for selecting parts of polynomials see the Reduce manual.

4.5 To make decisions with boolean operators

For flow control in a program it is very useful to determine properties of expressions[10] and to compare expressions somehow. The prefix and infix operators instrumental for deciding how to continue a computation.

The following infix operators compare expressions or numbers:

EQUAL or =

NEQ

GREATERP or > (arguments are numbers)

LESSP or <   "

LEQ or <=   "

GEQ or >=   "

Several prefix operators exist that check if certain properties of expressions are true:

NUMBERP *expression*, true if *expression* is a number

FIXP *expression*, true if *expression* is an integer

FREEOF(*expression*, *variable*), true if *expression* does not contain *variable*

For more boolean operators, see the Reduce manual.

4.6 Writing messages

In complex programs it is sometimes useful to write informal messages, warnings, or to abort the computation with a fatal error message. Reduce provides commands for this purpose.

WRITE $item_1, \ldots item_n$;

evaluates and prints $item_i$ if it is an expression or an assignment; if it is a string of characters enclosed by double quotes, the string is simply printed. Examples are:

```
WRITE "START PROGRAM";
IF FIXP(N) AND N>0
  THEN FOR L:=2:N PRODUCT L
  ELSE WRITE N," IS NOT A POSITIVE INTEGER!";
WRITE B:=E**X," WAS ASSIGNED";
```

---

[10] Recall that an expression is a sequence of numbers, variables, operators, parenthesis and commas.

```
ARRAY ONE(10);
FOR L:=0:10 DO
        << ONE(L):=L**2;
           WRITE "ELEMENT ",L," IS ",ONE(L)>>;
```

To print an error message and to abort your program, use

REDERR *string*

Here is an example using the previously defined function

$$fct = \frac{(x+1)^2 \sin x}{x^3 + 13x^2 + 50x + 56} :$$

```
FCT:=(X+1)**2*SIN(X)/(X**3+13*X**2+50*X+56);

IF SUB(X=-10,DEN FCT)=0
   THEN REDERR "ZERO DENOMINATOR"
   ELSE SUB(X=-10,FCT);

IF SUB(X=-7,DEN FCT)=0
   THEN REDERR "ZERO DENOMINATOR"
   ELSE SUB(X=-7,FCT);
```

4.7 How to define your own operators

In addition to those operators built into the Reduce system, the user may create new operators on his own with the statement

OPERATOR *operatorname*$_1$, ... *operatorname*$_n$;

No arguments are specified in the declaration statement. After the declaration, the specified operators may be used with arguments, just like SIN, COS, etc.:

```
CLEAR F,L,N;
OPERATOR F;
F(L);
F(N):=N**4+H**3+P**2+U;
F(4,K):=G;
```

If an operator is given with a certain argument, say F(N), and an expression (here N**4+H**3+P**2+U, which contains the argument N of the operator) is assigned to the operator F(N), this is a specific assignment only. There is *no* general functional relationship established between the argument of the operator and the same identifier which appears in the assigned expression. Such a relationship can only be created by LET rules, which will be discussed in Sects.4.8 and 5.1. Let us demonstrate this somewhat difficult point as follows:

```
F(N):=N**4+H**3+P**2+U;
F(L);                        % does not evaluate to the value
                             % L**4+H**3+P**2+U, but only to F(L)
F(N);                        % again yields N**4+H**3+P**2+U
```

A newly created operator, which has no previously assigned value, carries as value its own name with the arguments (in contrast to the elements of an array which are initialized with value zero and which can never have as values the array name with their indices!). These operators have no properties, unless LET rules are specified.

Example: Create an operator named LOG10 for log_{10} , and define the values for $log_{10} 1$, $log_{10} 10$, $log_{10} 100$:

```
OPERATOR LOG10;                      % declare LOG10 as operator
LOG10(1):=0;                         % assign 0 to LOG10(1)
LOG10(10):=1;
LOG10(100):=2;

LOG10(50+2*20+10);                   % test LOG10
LOG10((X+3*Y)**2)*LOG10(10)+LOG10(1);
LOG10(1000);
```

4.8 LET rules

In the last section we learnt that a user-defined operator, called with a certain argument, can only evaluate to a certain expression if such an assignment has been made earlier. It would be useful, however, to define general rules for an operator such that the operator, if evaluated, acts on its arguments and yields a certain expression. For example, the operator log_{10} shown above, which is intended to represent the logarithm to the base 10, should evaluate, of course, to n if the argument is 10^n.

Reduce provides a mechanism to define such rules for operators and variables using the LET statement. Its simplest form reads:

LET *substitution list*

where *substitution list* is a list of rules separated by commas, each of the form

variable = expression

or

prefix-operator(argument$_1$ ... argument$_n$) = expression

or

$argument_1$ *infix-operator* $argument_2$ = *expression.*

Hence an equivalent definition of our operator LOG10 using LET (still without general rules for the arguments) could read:

```
OPERATOR LOG10;                    % if not already declared
LET LOG10(1)=0,LOG10(10)=1,LOG10(100)=2;
```

Try the following example:

```
LTEST:=LOG(L)*SIN(L)*LOG10(L);
L:=10;                             % you may of course type LET L=10;
LTEST;                             % the result reads LOG(10)*SIN(10)
```

In the same way it is possible to define rules for infix operators:

```
CLEAR X,A,B,W;
LET X=Y;
LET A*B=C,L+M=N;
LET W**3=Y**2;
```

Accordingly, X**5+1 will evaluate to Y**5+1. The rule A*B=C means that whenever both, A and B, are factors in an expression, their product will be replaced by C. For example, A**3*C*B**6; evaluates to B**3*C**4.

In contrast to rules with products, Reduce will interpret an expression containing +, -, and / according to the rule that all but the first term of the left–hand–side has to be moved to the right–hand–side. Example: The rule L+M=N will not only replace terms L+M whenever they occur by N, but also L by N-M. Type

```
L*(L+M);
```

and it will evaluate to (N-M)*N. The rule W**3=Y**2 will apply to any power of W greater than or equal to the third:

```
W**4*Y;             % evaluates to   W*Y**3
W**2*Y;             % evaluates to   W**2*Y
```

Type in

```
LET Z**4=0;
```

and see what happens:

```
Z**3;               % evaluates to   Z**3
Z**5;               % evaluates to   0
Z**N;               % evaluates to   Z**N
```

These simple LET rules are on the same logical level as assignments made by := . An assignment X:=P+Q cancels a rule LET X=Y**2 made earlier, and vice versa.

Be cautious, since rules may be recursive, what we will use later on. Hence it is possible to define rules like

```
LET X=X+1;
```

If X is subsequently evaluated, it will lead to an infinite loop because the evaluation cannot find a legal end:

X evaluates to X+1 evaluates to (X+1)+1 evaluates to ...

Important examples for the use of LET rules are functional relations between trigonometric functions:

```
LET (SIN V)**2 + (COS V)**2 = 1;
```

```
4*(SIN V)**2 + 4*(COS V)**2;   % evaluates to    4
4*(SIN V)**2 + 2*(COS V)**2;   % evaluates to    4-2*(COS V)**2
4*(SIN Z)**2 + 4*(COS Z)**2;   % evaluates to
                               %     4*(SIN Z)**2+4*(COS Z)**2
4*(SIN Z)**2 + 2*(COS Z)**2;   % evaluates to
                               %     4*(SIN Z)**2+2*(COS Z)**2
```

The above LET rule forces Reduce to replace every occurrence of (SIN V)**2 in every expression by 1-(COS V)**2. As you can see from the last two examples, our rule defined matches only with SIN V, but not with SIN Z.

4.9 Homework

- Determine the first 10 coefficients of the Taylor expansion for $log(x^3 + 3) \, sin \, x$ at $x = 0$. Use your Taylor expansion program of Sect.3.8. Select the 4th coefficient.

- Determine whether $y(x) = 4x^4 + 3x^3 + 2x^2 + 1$ has any inflection points.

- Let there be given the ellipse $\frac{x^2}{a^2} + \frac{y^2}{b^2} = 1$. Determine the rectangle of maximum area within the ellipse.

- Calculate dy/dx in terms of x and y for the function $y(x)$ which is implicitly given by $x^2 + y^2 - 4x + 3y - 2 = 0$.

- Define a new operator DELTA with the properties of the Kronecker $\delta_{ij}, i, j = 0, 1, 2, 3$. Initialize DELTA with the LET statement.

- Compute the Bernoulli numbers B_n from the equation

$$\frac{t}{e^t - 1} = \sum_{n=0}^{\infty} \frac{B_n t^n}{n!}$$

(Hint: Show that

$$t = \sum_{n=1}^{\infty} \frac{t^n}{n!} \times \sum_{n=0}^{\infty} \frac{B_n t^n}{n!} = \sum_{n=0}^{\infty} \sum_{k=0}^{n} \frac{B_k}{(n-k)!k!} t^n - \sum_{n=0}^{\infty} \frac{B_n t^n}{n!} \,,$$

and compare the coefficients.)

- Verify that $z = (x+y)^3 - 12xy$ has stationary points in $(0,0)$ and $(1,1)$. Is it a minimum, a maximum or a saddle point?

Lecture 5

5.1 Extended LET rules

In lecture 4 we introduced user–defined operators in order to handle mathematical functions that Reduce does not provide. But, as the last example of Sect.4.8 shows, the LET rules described still don't provide for the general replacement of arbitrary arguments. However, we want to replace, for instance, $sin^2 x + cos^2 x$ by 1 for an arbitrary variable x. For this purpose we have the following two types of extended LET statements:

> FOR ALL $argument_1, \ldots argument_n$ LET $sustitution\ list$

or

> FOR ALL $argument_1, \ldots argument_n$ SUCH THAT $condition$ LET $sustitution\ list$

$Substitution\ list$ has been defined in Sect.4.8; it may be, for instance, a relation of the type $argument_1$ $infix\text{-}operator$ $argument_2 = expression$.

The first type allows us to create general rules. $Argument_1, \ldots argument_n$ must appear in every rule contained in the substitution list. They specify arbitrary arguments of operators. Accordingly, the rule

> FOR ALL X LET (SIN X)**2+(COS X)**2=1;

also matches (SIN Z)**2+(COS Z)**2, since it is defined FOR ALL X. You may wonder what happens if you type

> 4*(SIN Z)**2 + 2*(COS Z)**2;

It evaluates to 4-2*(COS Z)**2, because Reduce moves, according to the LET rule defined, (COS Z)**2 to the right, and (SIN Z)**2 is substituted by the right–hand-side, as has been described in Sect.4.8.

Let us return to the operator log_{10}. In Reduce we can create a set of rules for its products, quotients, and exponents as follows:

```
OPERATOR LOG10;
FOR ALL N,M LET LOG10(N*M)=LOG10(N)+LOG10(M),
            LOG10(N/M)=LOG10(N)-LOG10(M),
            LOG10(M**N)=N*LOG10(M);
A:=X**2*Y/Z**6;
LOG10(A);          % evaluates to 2*LOG10(X)+LOG10(Y)-6*LOG10(Z)
B:=LOG10(Z**6);
LOG10(A*B);        % evaluates to 2*LOG10(X)+LOG10(Y)-6*LOG10(Z)
                   %          + LOG10(6) + LOG10(LOG10(Z))
```

5.2 Examples: Factorials and binomial coefficients

The second type of an extended LET statement is used if a rule only applys under certain conditions. Write, for example, an operator to compute factorials:

```
OPERATOR FACTORIAL;
FOR ALL N SUCH THAT FIXP N AND N >= 0
    LET FACTORIAL(N) = FOR K:=1:N PRODUCT K;
```

```
FACTORIAL(7);                   % evaluates to 5040
FACTORIAL(U);                   % evaluates to FACTORIAL(U)
FACTORIAL(4/3);                 % evaluates to FACTORIAL(4/3)
FACTORIAL(8/2);                 % evaluates to 24
```

Obviously the rule applies only if the operator's argument is an integer ≥ 0; recall the operator FIXP of Sect.4.5.

As a further exercise we can define an operator for computing Legendre polynomials according to the rule

$$P_n(x) = \frac{1}{n!} \frac{d^n}{dy^n} \frac{1}{\sqrt{y^2 - 2xy + 1}}\bigg|_{y=0}$$

We use the operator FACTORIAL that we have just defined:

```
CLEAR Y;
OPERATOR PN;
FOR ALL X,N SUCH THAT FIXP N
    LET PN(X,N)=SUB(Y=0,DF(1/SQRT(Y**2-2*X*Y+1),Y,N))
                        /FACTORIAL(N);
PN(X,3);
PN(X,N);
```

LET rules, in conformity with the structure of the underlying Lisp language, may be stated in a recursive manner. We will define, in an alternative way, a new factorial operator using its recursion formula:

```
OPERATOR FACTORIA1;
FOR ALL N SUCH THAT FIXP N AND N > 1
    LET FACTORIA1(N) = N*FACTORIA1(N-1);
LET FACTORIA1(1)=1;
LET FACTORIA1(0)=1;
```

```
FACTORIA1(3);                   % evaluates to 6
```

FACTORIA1 is called with an integer argument, here 3. Therefore, according to the first LET statement, the product of the argument 3 and FACTORIA1(3-1) is computed once

`FACTORIA1(2)` has been evaluated. Since `FACTORIA1(2)` evaluates to `2*FACTORIA1(1)` and, according to the LET rule `FACTORIA1(1)=1`, the product `3*2*1` is computed and returned as the value of `FACTORIA1(3)`. The rule LET `FACTORIA1(1)=1` is always the exit condition for the other (recursive) LET rule.

Let us now come back to our problem with the logarithms. We still want to program the evaluation rule for $log_{10} 10^n = n$, $n > 0$:

```
LET LOG10(1)=0;
FOR ALL N
      LET LOG10(10**N)=N;
FOR ALL N SUCH THAT FIXP N AND N>0 AND FIXP (N/10)
      LET LOG10(N)=LOG10(N/10) + 1;
```

We test our operator with $log_{10} 200$, $log_{10} 345$, $log_{10} \frac{23}{3700}$, $log_{10} 20^b$, $log_{10} 20^3$:

```
LOG10(200);
LOG10(345);
LOG10(23/3700);   % is also expanded if the rule for / is present
LOG10(20**V);     % what happens without assigning a value to B?
V:=3;
LOG10(20**V);
```

The operator `LOG10` in this example is recursive. The evaluation of `LOG10` always stops if the argument divided by 10 is not an integer. Of course, you could program an equivalent operator `LOG10` which stops if the argument is smaller than 1.

Next let us turn to an operator for $bin(n,p) := \binom{n}{p}$, which evaluates to the binomial coefficient, provided n and p are integers. Verify by means of this operator the well-known rules

$$\binom{n}{p} + \binom{n}{p+1} = \binom{n+1}{p+1}$$

$$\binom{n}{p} \cdot \frac{n-p}{p+1} = \binom{n}{p+1}$$

For this purpose, we first define the operator `FACTORIA2` such that `FACTORIA2(N+M)` evaluates to

$$\text{FACTORIA2(N)} * (N+1)*(N+2)*\ldots*(N+M-1)*(N+M) \quad \textit{if } M > 0$$

or

$$\text{FACTORIA2(N)} / N/(N-1)/\ldots/(N+M+2)/(N+M+1) \quad \textit{if } M < 0.$$

This mechanism leads to a normalized form of `FACTORIA2` and allows Reduce to cancel equivalent coefficients in the numerator and the denominator:

```
OPERATOR FACTORIA2,BIN;


%definition for FACTORIA2
FOR ALL N,M SUCH THAT FIXP(M) AND M NEQ 0
      LET FACTORIA2(N+M)=IF M>0
                          THEN FACTORIA2(N+M-1)*(N+M)
                          ELSE FACTORIA2(N+M+1)/(N+M+1);
%test it:
FACTORIA2(K+5);   % evaluates to FACTORIA2(K)*(K**5 + 15*K**4
                  %        + 85*K**3 + 225*K**2 + 274*K + 120)


FACTORIA2(K-5);   % evaluates to FACTORIA2(K)/(K*(K**4
                  %        - 10*K**3 + 35*K**2 - 50*K + 24))



%definition for BIN
FOR ALL N,P
      LET BIN(N,P)=FACTORIA2(N)/(FACTORIA2(P)*FACTORIA2(N-P));

% now verify:
BIN(N,P)+BIN(N,P+1)-BIN(N+1,P+1);      % should be 0
BIN(N,P)*(N-P)/(P+1)-BIN(N,P+1);       % should be 0
```

5.3 Clearing LET rules

As mentioned in Sect.1.1, it is sometimes necessary to remove the assigned value
from a variable or expression. In the same manner it is also necessary to clear LET rules
which we don't want to be active any longer. To remove assignments and substitution
rules the CLEAR operator is used. The first form is:

CLEAR $expression_1$, ... $expression_n$;

Thereby any assignments of $expression_1$,...$expression_n$ are removed. Examples are

```
A:=(X+Y)**2;
U:=A+(R+S)**2;
X:=1;
A;                         % evaluates to (1+Y)**2
U;                         % evaluates to (1+Y)**2 + (R+S)**2;
CLEAR X;
A;                         % evaluates to (X+Y)**2;
U;                         % evaluates to (X+Y)**2 + (R+S)**2;
CLEAR A;
```

```
A;                            % evaluates to A
U;                            % evaluates to (X+Y)**2 + (R+S)**2;
```

It is *not* possible to clear a single array element,

```
ARRAY A(7);
FOR L:=0:7 DO A(L):=(X+1)**L;
CLEAR A(5);                         % returns the error message...
                             % ***** substitution for 5 not allowed
FOR L:=0:7 DO WRITE A(L);          % A(5) is not cleared
```

rather you can clear the whole array (it will then be undeclared):

```
CLEAR A;
A(6);                              % returns the message...
                             % declare  a  operator? (Y or N)
```

LET rules are removed by repeating the corresponding LET statement, using CLEAR in place of LET and omitting the equal sign and the expression on its right–hand–side. The same dummy variables must be used in the FOR ALL part, and the boolean expression in the SUCH THAT part must be written the same way. The LET rules

```
FOR ALL N SUCH THAT FIXP N AND N > 1
       LET FACTORIA1(N) = N*FACTORIA1(N-1);
LET FACTORIA1(1)=1;
LET FACTORIA1(0)=1;
```

can be removed by the commands

```
FOR ALL N SUCH THAT FIXP N AND N > 1
       CLEAR FACTORIA1(N);
CLEAR FACTORIA1(1), FACTORIA1(0);
FACTORIA1(7);               % is unknown to the system
```

If desired, a whole operator can be cleared by mentioning its name in the CLEAR statement, as in

```
CLEAR FACTORIA1;
```

The corresponding LET rules don't get lost. If later the operator is defined again, the LET rules are still active. Hence you may remove these rules, too.

5.4 Creating non–commutative algebras, symmetric and antisymmetric operators

In Reduce, operators may be declared to have additional properties, such as non-commutativity under multiplication, by the declaration

```
NONCOM operatorname₁,...operatornameₙ;
```

An example reads:

```
OPERATOR X,P;
NONCOM X,P;
X(I)*P(J)-P(J)*X(I);        % does not evaluate to 0
X(I)*P(J)+P(J)*X(I);        % does not evaluate to 2*X(I)*P(J)
```

Operators can be declared symmetric or antisymmetric by

SYMMETRIC $operatorname_1$, . . . $operatorname_n$;

or

ANTISYMMETRIC $operatorname_1$, . . . $operatorname_n$;

Then in each expression the arguments of the symmetric and antisymmetric operators are reordered in order to conform with the internal order used by Reduce. An example would be

```
OPERATOR COMM;
ANTISYMMETRIC COMM;
COMM(X,P)+COMM(P,X);        % should evaluate to 0
```

Example:[11] Consider, in Cartesian coordinates, the position and the momentum operators x_i and p_i of a quantum mechanical system. Note that $x^2 = x_1{}^2 + x_2{}^2 + x_3{}^2$ (an analogous expression is valid for p^2). Start with the commutators $[x_i, p_j] = i\hbar\delta_{ij}$ and calculate $[x^2, p_j]$ as well as $[x_i, p^2]$.

```
OPERATOR X,P,COMM,DELTA;
NONCOM X,P;
ANTISYMMETRIC COMM;

FOR ALL A,B SUCH THAT A NEQ B AND NUMBERP A AND NUMBERP B
                LET DELTA(A,B)=0;
FOR ALL A       LET DELTA(A,A)=1;

FOR ALL A,B,C  LET COMM(X(A),X(B))=0,
                COMM(P(A),P(B))=0,
                COMM(X(A),P(B))=HBAR*I*DELTA(A,B),
                COMM(A+B,C)    =COMM(A,C)  +COMM(B,C),
                COMM(A**2,B)   =A*COMM(A,B)+COMM(A,B)*A;

X2:=FOR L:=1:3 SUM X(L)**2;
P2:=FOR L:=1:3 SUM P(L)**2;

FOR L:=1:3 COLLECT COMM(X2,P(L));
FOR L:=1:3 COLLECT COMM(P2,X(L));
```

---

[11] Note that according to a Reduce *bug*, the result may not be computed correctly with Reduce versions older than January 1988.

5.5 Procedures for repeated use of commands

It is often useful to name a statement for repeated use in calculations with varying parameters, or to define a complete evaluation procedure for an operator. For this purpose, Reduce offers the procedure declaration statement

PROCEDURE *procedurename* (*variable*$_1$, ... *variable*$_n$); *statement*;

Thereby a procedure named *procedurename* is created with the formal parameters *variable*$_1$, ... *variable*$_n$. The *statement* in the procedure declaration is called the procedure body. It defines what the procedure, if called, actually does.

The procedure is called by *procedurename* and the list of the actual parameters. Then the formal parameters used in the procedure body are substituted by the values of the actual parameters used in the procedure call. Note that, unlike operators, procedures always evaluate to a value, the value of *statement*.

Example: Write a procedure for the Taylor series.

```
CLEAR X,P;
PROCEDURE TAYLOR (FUNC, X, XO, N);
SUB(X=XO,FUNC) + FOR K:=1:N SUM SUB(X=XO,DF(FUNC,X,K))
                    * (X-XO)**K / FOR J:=1:K PRODUCT J ;


ON DIV;
TAYLOR(  E**Y, Y, 0, 4);
TAYLOR( SIN Z, Z, 0, 5);
OFF DIV;
```

If more than one statement is required, use the group or the compound statement. *Example:* Write a procedure that computes the finite integral $\int_{x_0}^{x_1} f(x)dx$. Calculate $\int_0^1 (x^3 + x^2)dx$ and $\int_0^\pi \frac{y}{\sqrt{y^2+1}}dy$.

```
LOAD INT,ALGINT;                  % if necessary


PROCEDURE FINT(F,X,XO,X1);
BEGIN SCALAR VAL;
    VAL:=INT(F,X);
    RETURN SUB(X=X1,VAL)-SUB(X=XO,VAL);
END;


FINT(X**3+X**2,X,0,1);
FINT(Y/SQRT(Y**2+1),Y,0,PI);
```

If procedures have no arguments, empty parentheses may be optionally used in the procedure header, but they must be specified in the procedure call. Write, for example, a procedure that turns off the switche EXP and turns on the switch GCD, and the corresponding inverse procedure:

```
PROCEDURE FACTON();              % with empty parentheses
<<ON GCD; OFF EXP>>;
PROCEDURE FACTOFF;               % without parentheses
<<OFF GCD; ON EXP>>;

POL:=(B+C)**3;
FACTON();                        % parentheses necessary
POL;
FACTOFF();                       % parentheses necessary
POL;
```

Like operators, procedures may also be defined recursively. Another version of the factorial is

```
PROCEDURE FACTORIA3(N);
IF FIXP N AND N>=0
    THEN ( IF N<2
             THEN 1
             ELSE N*FACTORIA3(N-1) )
    ELSE REDERR("ILLEGAL ARGUMENT !");
```

The procedure call to FACTORIA3 will either lead to an error, if the argument is not a legal argument, or will compute the factorial recursively in the same way as in Sect.5.2. During the first step of the procedure, FACTORIA3(3) will evaluate to 3*FACTORIA3(2). In the second step FACTORIA3(2) is evaluated and the whole value results in 3*2*FACTORIA3(1). Finally FACTORIA3(1) is determined and the processing stops, returning the result 6. Never forget to define a legal end for recursions!

5.6 A procedure for l'Hospital's rule and a caveat

Now we return to our first example in Sect.1.1 in order to write a procedure for applying the l'Hospital rule. Test the procedure with the help of the following examples:

$$\frac{x^3 \sin x}{(1 - \cos x)^2}\bigg|_{x=0},$$

$$\frac{(1+x)^n - (1-x)^n}{e^{1+x} - e^{1-x}}\bigg|_{x=0},$$

$$\frac{\log(x^{2m} + x^m - 1) - m \log x}{x^2 - 1}\bigg|_{x=1},$$

$$\frac{e^{ax} - e^{-bx}}{\log(1 + x)}\bigg|_{x=0},$$

$$\left(\frac{1}{\sin x} - \frac{x}{6} - \frac{1}{x}\right)\frac{1}{x^3}\bigg|_{x=0},$$

$$\frac{\sin^2 x}{x^3}\bigg|_{x=0}.$$

```
PROCEDURE HOSP(FUNCT,VAR,LIM);
IF SUB(VAR=LIM,DEN FUNCT)=0
   THEN IF SUB(VAR=LIM,NUM FUNCT)=0
           THEN HOSP(DF(NUM FUNCT,VAR)/DF(DEN FUNCT,VAR),VAR,LIM)
           ELSE REDERR "INFINITY"
   ELSE SUB(VAR=LIM,FUNCT);
```

```
HOSP(                    X**3*SIN(X)/(1-COS(X))**2,   X,   0);
HOSP(   ((1+X)**N-(1-X)**N)/(E**(1+X)-E**(1-X)),      X,   0);
HOSP(   (LOG(X**(2*M)+X**M-1)-M*LOG(X))/(X**2-1),     X,   1);
HOSP(            (E**(A*X)-E**(-B*X))/LOG(1+X),       X,   0);
HOSP(                  (1/SIN(X)-X/6-1/X)/X**3,       X,   0);
HOSP(                            SIN(X)**2/X**3,      X,   0);
```

Now we turn to the caveat. If we intend to write a procedure which assigns the 1st, 2nd, and 3rd derivative of an expression $ex(x)$ to the three variables v_1, v_2, v_3, we might try

```
PROCEDURE DFEX (EX,X,V1,V2,V3);
<< V1:=DF(EX,X);
   V2:=DF(V1,X);
   V3:=DF(V2,X) >>;
```

```
DFEX(E**(Z**2),Z,D1,D2,D3);
D1;
```

However, it doesn't work! The assignment statements are bound to fail, because (although the procedure is called by value) the left–hand–side V1 of the assignment V1:=DF(EX,X) is *not* evaluated. Therefore at this point, when V1 only exists within the procedure body, the assignment statement is interpreted as V1:=DF(E**Z,Z), rather than as D1:=DF(E**Z,Z) as we might have expected. In such a case we can use the SET statement,

SET(*left*, *right*)

which, in contrast to the operator := , assigns the value of *right* to the value(!) of *left*. Accordingly, our procedure should be written as

```
PROCEDURE DFEX (EX,X,V1,V2,V3);
<< SET(V1,DF(EX,X));
   SET(V2,DF(V1,X));
```

```
    SET(V3,DF(V2,X)) >>;

DFEX(E**(Z**2),Z,D1,D2,D3);
D2;
```

Incidentally, the SET statement can not only be used in the body of a procedure, but also in an ordinary command "on the toplevel":

```
CLEAR A,B,C;
POL:=(X+Y)**3;
A:=B+C;
SET(A-C,POL);
B;
```

It assigns the value of POL to B.

5.7 Homework

• The Legendre polynomials may be defined recursively by

$$P_n(x) = \frac{1}{n}\left(x(2n-1)P_{n-1}(x) - (n-1)P_{n-2}(x)\right) \quad \text{with} \quad P_0(x) = 1, \quad P_1(x) = x.$$

Define a recursive operator for $P_n(x)$.

• Define an operator CC which determines the complex conjugate part of an arbitrary expression. Define CC rules for expressions which involve operators such as + - * / ** SIN COS etc., as, for instance, $\overline{x+y} = \bar{x} + \bar{y}$, $\overline{\sin x} = \sin \bar{x}$. Don't forget rules for handling all integers. In addition, define operators RE and IM to determine the real and imaginary part of an expression. Use the identities $Im(x) = (x - \bar{x})/2i$ and $Re(x) = (x + \bar{x})/2$. Write procedures that may declare single expressions to be purely real or purely imaginary. Test IM, RE, and CC by using the following expressions:

$$a = 4 + 3i$$
$$b = 4z + 3ix$$
$$c = \sin b$$
$$d = e^b$$
$$f = 1/b^2$$
$$g = a/b$$

Observe that all unassigned variables appearing on the right–hand–sides might be complex.

- Define an operator INTE to compute the integral

$$I_n = \int_0^1 x^n e^x \, dx \, ,$$

by using the recursion formula $I_n = e - nI_{n-1}$, with $I_1 = 1$.

- Continue with the computation of quantum mechanical operators (compare Sect.5.4). The angular momentum operator is defined by $l_i = \varepsilon_{ijk}[x_j, p_k]$. Verify $[l_1, l_2] = i\hbar l_3$ and determine $[l_3, l^2]$ and $[l_3, l_z^2]$. (Hints: Define new operators EPS for the Levi–Civita symbol ε_{ijk} and L for the angular momentum. Note that ε_{ijk} is, by definition, equal to $+1$, -1, 0 depending whether $(i\,j\,k)$ is an even, an odd, or no permutation of $(1\,2\,3)$, respectively.)

- The procedure for computing the Taylor series is very slow for large expressions since in each step of the for loop the $(n+1)$st derivative of the function must be computed completely, even though the nth derivative is known from the previous step. Write an improved procedure by using in each step the result of the previous step.

Lecture 6

6.1 Linear algebra package: Matrices

The matrix package of Reduce is a very powerful feature for $(m \times n)$ matrix calculations. Matrices are declared by

MATRIX $matrix_1, matrix_2, \ldots matrix_n$;

where $matrix_i$ are the matrices to be declared. If the dimensions of the matrices are already known before initialization, the sizes may be also given in the declaration statement:

MATRIX VECT(4,1),M(4,4),K,N(4,4);

Here VECT is declared as a (column) vector, that is, as a (4×1) matrix, M and N as (4×4) matrices, and K as a matrix with a size still to be specified. The numbering of the elements of a matrix starts at 1, not at 0, as in the case of an array. Initially the matrix elements have zero values. They are referred to like elements of an array:

```
VECT(2,1);
VECT(3,1)*M(3,2);
4+3*N(2,4);
```

To change the value of a matrix element, only a simple assignment statement is needed:

```
VECT(1,1):=(X+Y)**2;
            .
            .
            .
VECT(4,1):=25;
```

If the size of a matrix has not been specified in the declaration, the MAT operator must be used for assigning values to the elements of an $(l \times n)$ matrix in order to let Reduce know what the size of the matrix is:

$matrix$:= MAT($(m_{11}, m_{12}, \ldots, m_{1n})$,
$\qquad\qquad\qquad (m_{21}, m_{22}, \ldots, m_{2n})$,
$\qquad\qquad\qquad\qquad .$
$\qquad\qquad\qquad\qquad .$
$\qquad\qquad\qquad\qquad .$
$\qquad\qquad\qquad (m_{l1}, m_{l2}, \ldots, m_{ln})$);

Observe that single rows of the matrix are separated by parentheses. In the example

```
K:=MAT( (A,25,0*P),
        (L,67,0+P)  );
```

K is defined as a (2×3) matrix.

A matrix may be referred to as a whole merely by using the matrix name in an expression. Moreover the usual well–known algebraic operations for matrices are defined in Reduce provided the matrices are of compatible size, as, for example, in

```
MATRIX M(4,4),N(4,4);                  % if not declared earlier
M(1,1):=-1; M(2,2):=M(3,3):=M(4,4):=1;
N(1,1):=A; N(2,2):=B; N(3,3):=C; N(4,4):=D; N(2,4):=1;
M*N;
M+N;
M-N;
N:=N**3;
M**(-1);
M/N;                    % this is understood as M * (N**(-1))
```

Arrays differ from matrices in that an array can only be used as a variable *with* indices. The previous example, in array notation, would read:

```
ARRAY MA(3,3),NA(3,3),MATIMESNA(3,3),MAPLUSNA(3,3);

MA(0,0):=-1; MA(1,1):=MA(2,2):=MA(3,3):=1;
NA(0,0):=ALPHA; NA(1,1):=BETA; NA(2,2):=GAMMA; NA(3,3):=DELTA;
NA(1,3):=1;

FOR I:=0:3 DO FOR J:=0:3 DO                  % multiplication
    MATIMESNA(I,J) := FOR K:=0:3 SUM MA(I,K)*NA(K,J);

FOR I:=0:3 DO FOR J:=0:3 DO                  % addition
    MAPLUSNA(I,J)  := MA(I,J)+NA(I,J);
```

Clearly, the matrix package is more convenient. However, for quantities of higher rank (that is with more than two indices) like the Christoffel symbols or the Riemannian curvature tensor, arrays are indispensible.

A typical task for the matrix package would be to find the general solution for the system of four linear equations

$$
\begin{pmatrix} a_{11} & a_{12} & a_{13} & a_{14} \\ a_{21} & a_{22} & a_{23} & a_{24} \\ a_{31} & a_{32} & a_{33} & a_{34} \\ a_{41} & a_{42} & a_{43} & a_{44} \end{pmatrix} \times \begin{pmatrix} x_1 \\ x_2 \\ x_3 \\ x_4 \end{pmatrix} = \begin{pmatrix} b_1 \\ b_2 \\ b_3 \\ b_4 \end{pmatrix} .
$$

```
% Initialize matrices:
MATRIX AM(4,4),BM(4,1),XM(4,1);
OPERATOR AO,BO;                            % initialize
FOR L:=1:4 DO FOR N:=1:4 DO AM(L,N):=AO(L,N); % matrix AM and
FOR L:=1:4 DO BM(L,1):=BO(L);              % vector BM

% Solve the linear system
XM:=AM**(-1) * BM;
```

The numbers of rows and columns of a given matrix can be calculated by

```
LENGTH(matrix)
```

A list with the corresponding numbers is returned. Try, for instance,

```
LENGTH AM;
```

Additionally, some often used operators in matrix calculations are available. The transposed matrix can be determined by

```
TP(matrix)
```

An example is:

```
TP N;
```

The trace of a square matrix is formed by

```
TRACE(matrix)
```

as in

```
TRACE(K*(TP K));
```

and its determinant by

```
DET(matrix)
```

such as in

```
DET (K * (TP K));
```

Example: Determine the eigenvalues of the matrix $\begin{pmatrix} -2 & 5 & 4 \\ 5 & 7 & 5 \\ 4 & 5 & -2 \end{pmatrix}$.

```
MATRIX M(3,3),MM(3,3);
M:=MAT( (-2, 5, 4),
        ( 5, 7, 5),
        ( 4, 5,-2) );
FOR L:=1:3 DO MM(L,L):=M(L,L)-Y;
SOLVE(DET(MM),Y);
```

alternatively, we can use the *experimental* operator

> MATEIGEN(*matrix, variable*)

which yields a list with three items: the eigenvalue equation, the multiplicity of the eigenvalues, and the eigenvectors themselves. With the following chain of commands we can determine the eigenvalues and the eigenvectors of a given matrix:

```
MATRIX EIGVEC;
RESULT:=MATEIGEN(M,EIGVAL);
EIGVEC:=THIRD(FIRST(RESULT));
EVL:=SOLVE(FIRST(FIRST(RESULT)),EIGVAL);  % yields the eigenvalues
EIGVAL:=RHS(FIRST(EVL));                   % -3
EIGVEC;                                    % 1st eigenvector
EIGVAL:=RHS(SECOND(EVL));                  % -6
EIGVEC;                                    % 2nd eigenvector
EIGVAL:=RHS(THIRD(EVL));                   % 12
EIGVEC;                                    % 3rd eigenvector
```

But be careful: This operator is not yet officially integrated into Reduce. It might sometimes yield incorrect results, though we don't know of any.

The matrix package might not be implemented at all sites. Normally the matrix package is loaded automatically if matrices are used in computations. Otherwise try the command

> LOAD MATR;

If this doesn't work either, ask your local software manager!

6.2 Calculus of exterior differential forms in EXCALC

Exterior differential forms and the corresponding Cartan calculus are increasingly applied in classical mechanics and classical field theory, as well as in gauge theories and in general relativity and its extensions. The Excalc package of Reduce, which can be loaded according to the pattern

> LOAD EXCALC;

was devised by E. Schrüfer exactly for this purpose. Currently the package is able to handle scalar–valued differential forms, vectors and operations between them, as well as non–scalar valued, i.e. indexed forms. We have made extensive use of this package in our research, finding exact solutions in general relativity and gauge theories of gravitation.

It was mainly our research in gravitational gauge theories which has made us conscious of the fact that we had to learn CA. Since at those days (about 1982) Excalc

was not available, we started with A. Krasiński's Lisp–based program ORTOCAR-
TAN, which is quite useful. In our more recent research papers[12] , our tool is bare
Reduce (if the job extends to the limits of our hardware environment) or, preferably,
Reduce enriched by the Excalc package.

A form is declared by specifying its rank and its valence.

```
PFORM CHRIST1(A,B)=1;
```

declares CHRIST1 as a 1–form with 2 indices A and B[13] .

```
PFORM CURV2(A,B)=2;
```

declares CURV2 as a 2–form. It also has 2 indices. The names of the indices are
arbitrary, that is, we could have declared PFORM CURV2(I,J)=2 instead. An ordinary
function, a 0–form, must be declared as well:

```
PFORM PSI=0;
```

With

```
FDOMAIN PSI=PSI(R);
```

the function Ψ is declared to depend on the variable r. Hence @(PSI,THETA) , @
being the partial differentiation sign in Excalc in analogy to the DF of Reduce, will
now evaluate to zero.

The exterior differential, simply enough, is denoted by D, and the exterior product
sign by the wedge ^ . Then, using the declared forms we can, for instance, formulate
the following statement:

```
CURV2(-A,B):=D CHRIST1(-A,B)+CHRIST1(-C,B)^CHRIST1(-A,C);
```

The negative sign in front of an index signals that it is a subscript, i.e., a co–variant
index, whereas a positive sign (or no sign at all) marks a superscript, or a contravariant index. In Excalc the Einstein summation convention applies automatically,
with the result that Excalc sums over repeated indices in different positions, like
over -C and C in the example above. Note particularly that we do not need a FOR
statement for displaying all components of CURV2(A,B). A, B, and C run over the set
of the indices which were made known to the system by means of the declaration

```
INDEXRANGE T,R,THETA,PHI;
```

---

[12] See P. Baekler, M. Gürses, F.W. Hehl and J.D. McCrea: Physics Letters **A128**
(1988) 245-250; P. Baekler, M. Seitz and V. Winkelmann: Classical and Quantum
Gravity **5** (1988) 479-490.
[13] The number 1 in the identifier of the 1–form we have just put in for convenience to
remind us of the rank of the form.

for example, or by the coframe-command (see below).

The specific operators provided in Excalc are the following:

^	exterior multiplication	"nary" infix operator
D	exterior differentiation	unary prefix operator
@	partial differentiation	"nary" prefix operator
_|	inner product	binary infix operator
|_	Lie derivative	binary infix operator
#	Hodge star operator	unary prefix operator

Unary means that there is one, binary that there are two, and nary that there is any number of arguments.

Suppose we declare two vectors (tangent vectors) and a 2–form:

    TVECTOR V,W; PFORM F=2;

Then the inner product of V with W reads

    V _| F;

(the blanks are optional). Then the Lie derivative

    W |_ F;

evaluates to W _| D F + D(W _| F) as it should. In Excalc we can also perform a Lie derivative of a vector V with respect to another vector W, according to

    W |_ V;

Similarly to operators in bare Reduce, an indexed form like CHRIST1(A,B) can be declared to be antisymmetric under the exchange of its arguments:

    ANTISYMMETRIC CHRIST1;

There is a corresponding command for SYMMETRIC.

In order to inform Excalc of the dimension of the space we are working in, we declare

    SPACEDIM 4;

(or any other positive number). Now Excalc knows the range of the indices involved in the indexed p–forms declared above. If one works in 4–dimensional spacetime manifolds, the COFRAME–statement is enough to declare the dimension of the spacetime, the underlying 1–form basis and the signature of the metric. The corresponding vector basis, the FRAME, we denote by E. Let us take, for instance, the Minkowski spacetime of special relativity in spherical coordinates:

```
COFRAME   O(T)     =                        D T,
          O(R)     =                        D R,
          O(THETA) = R *              D THETA,
          O(PHI)   = R * SIN(THETA) * D PHI
     WITH SIGNATURE (1,-1,-1,-1);
FRAME E;
```

As a first case study for Excalc, we turn to Maxwell's equations of the electromagnetic field. Given the electromagnetic field-strength 2-form FARAD2 and the electromagnetic induction 2-form HMAX2 [14] , the left–hand–sides of the homogeneous and the inhomogeneous Maxwell equations read as follows:

```
PFORM FARAD2=2, HMAX2=2, MAXHOM3=3, MAXINH3=3;

FARAD2   := (Q/R**2)*O(T)^O(R); % a Coulomb field has been put in
MAXHOM3 := D FARAD2;            % l.h.s. of hom. Maxwell equ.

HMAX2    := # FARAD2;           % constitutive rel., here vacuum
MAXINH3 := D HMAX2;             % l.h.s. of inhom. Maxwell equ.

PFORM LMAX4=4, MAXENERGY3(A)=3;            % Lagrangian and energy

LMAX4            := -(1/2) * FARAD2 ^ HMAX2;
MAXENERGY3(-A) := E(-A) _| LMAX4 + (E(-A)_|FARAD2) ^ HMAX2;
```

The remarkable ease with which Excalc programs may be written is clearly shown in this example.

As a final example, we display an Excalc toy program for checking the correctness of the Schwarzschild solution with cosmological constant. We introduce at each point of the spacetime manifold a vector basis, the frame E(-A), see above, and the dual 1-form basis, the coframe O(A). Then, in Schwarzschild coordinates, we have

```
PFORM PSI=0; FDOMAIN PSI=PSI(R);
COFRAME O(T)     = PSI *            D T,
        O(R)     = (1/PSI) *        D R,
        O(THETA) = R *              D THETA,
        O(PHI)   = R * SIN(THETA) * D PHI
     WITH SIGNATURE (1,-1,-1,-1);

DISPLAYFRAME;         % displays the coframe O(A) of 1-forms
FRAME E;              % the dual frame of vectors is named E(B)
```

---

[14] FARAD2 is built up from the electric and the magnetic fields (E, B) and HMAX2 from (D, H).

```
PSI := SQRT(1-2*M/R+(LAM/3)*R**2); % the Schwarzschild function

PFORM CHRIST1(A,B)=1, CURV2(A,B)=2; ANTISYMMETRIC CHRIST1, CURV2;

CHRIST1(-A,-B):=-(1/2)*( E(-A)_|(E(-C)_|(D O(-B)))
                        -E(-B)_|(E(-A)_|(D O(-C)))
                        +E(-C)_|(E(-B)_|(D O(-A))) )*O(C);
CURV2(-A,B) := D CHRIST1(-A,B) + CHRIST1(-C,B) ^ CHRIST1(-A,C)$
ON GCD;
CURV2(A,B) := CURV2(A,B);

PFORM EINSTEIN3(A)=3;    % EPS represents the Levi-Civita symbol
EINSTEIN3(-A):=CURV2(B,C)^(EPS(-A,-B,-C,-D)*O(D));
END;
```

E. Schrüfer is presently (March 1989) upgrading the Excalc package. In particular, a variational derivative will be supported with respect to index–carrying quantities. Then, for instance, we can determine MAXENERGY3(-A), the engergy-momentum 3–form, directly from the Lagrangian 4-form LMAX4 via

```
MAXENERGY3(-A) := VARDF( LMAX4, O(A) );
```

This feature will be quite an achievement and will further enhance the power of Excalc.

6.3 Turning switches on and off

One aspect of symbolic computation that has still not been thoroughly discussed, is the display and structuring of expressions. Output formats are controlled by switches which may be turned ON and OFF:

ON $switch_1, \ldots switch_n$;

OFF $switch_1, \ldots switch_n$;

In the following, the most important switches are discussed. For more information on switches see the Reduce manual. To illustrate the use of switches, we provide the test expression

```
CLEAR X,Y,Z,A;
TEST:=X**2*(Y**2+2*Y)+X*(Y**2+Z)/(2*A);
```

which should be used in the following manner:

```
TEST;
```

ON $switch$;   or   OFF $switch$;

```
TEST;
```

For each switch the output format will be described if the switch is turned ON. The defaults of the switches will be added in parenthesis.

- Simple factors are printed outside the parentheses:
  ON ALLFAC; (default: on)

- The denominators of expressions are searched for simple factors to make rational fractions and negative powers appear in the output:
  ON DIV; (default: off)

- Each term in any sum is printed on a separate line:
  ON LIST; (default: off)

- Parentheses in expressions are expanded:
  ON EXP; (default: on)

- Cancelling common factors in the numerators and denominators of expressions:
  ON GCD; (default: off)
  The combination
  ON GCD; OFF EXP;
  produces partially factorized expressions.

- When two rational functions are added, an expression over a common denominator results:
  ON MCD; (default: on)
  In order to avoid this, turn this switch off. Example:
  ```
  OFF MCD;
  Z:=(2*A*C-5*B*D)/C-2*(3*B-A*D)/D;     % no common denominator
  ON MCD;
  Z;                                    % common denominator C*D
  ```

- Force Reduce to use floating point numbers instead of integers:
  ON FLOAT; (default: off)
  If this switch is turned on, all integers used are converted to floating point numbers, and vice versa if turned off. Note that arithmetic with floating point numbers is not exact.

- The output is printed in natural form, exponents are raised etc.:
  ON NAT; (default: on)
  If turned off, the output is written as required for a Reduce input. Therefore the output can again be used later on as input, if written to a file (cf. OUT).

- If the Reduce input is read from an external file, the input is echoed to the terminal display:
  ON ECHO; (default: on)

- If an evaluation leads to zero, the value is *not* printed:
  `ON NERO;` (default: off)

- Reduce output is to be displayed on the terminal (or, in batch mode, to be printed to the standard output device):
  `ON OUTPUT;` (default: on)
  If all output is to be suppressed, turn the switch off (used, for example, during loading of files).

- The numerator and denominator of an expression will be printed in two–dimensional form, provided one line is sufficient for it:
  `ON RATPRI;` (default: on)
  If turned off, the output will be in a linear form.

- After each evaluation, the time used for the evaluation process is printed:
  `ON TIME;` (default: off)

6.4 Reordering expressions

The declaration `ORDER` may be used for ordering variables within terms of expressions to be printed:

> `ORDER` $variable_1, \ldots variable_n$;

The order of $variable_1, \ldots variable_n$ in this declaration determines the order of these variables with respect to each other within the single terms of the printed expressions. Consider the following example:

> ```
> TEST;
> ORDER Y,X;
> TEST;
> ```

A declared order may be reset to the system default by:

> `ORDER NIL;`

It is possible to separate expressions into terms involving fixed powers of especially declared variables or operators and a sum of the rest of the terms. To specify a variable or an operator to be printed in the described way,

> `FACTOR` $variable_1, \ldots variable_n$;

is used. The factoring flag can be removed by

> `REMFAC` $variable_1, \ldots variable_n$;

Example:

> `TEST;`

```
FACTOR X;
TEST;
```

Suppose a Reduce expression represents a broken rational function, some variables of which are marked by FACTOR. With the switch RAT turned on, the expression is printed with each factored subexpession of the numerator having its own denominator:

```
ON RAT;  (default: off)
```

Consider the example

```
REMFAC X;
TEST;
FACTOR X;
ON RAT;
TEST;
```

6.5 On Reduce input and output

Usually an algebraic expression to be printed will fill the whole output line with terms. The length of the output line is controlled by the operator

```
LINELENGTH(n);
```

If an integer argument n is specified, the linelength is set to that new value, returning the old linelength as the value of LINELENGTH. If no argument is specified (or NIL), the current value of the linelength is returned. Example:

```
LINELENGTH(NIL);
ON EXP;
TEST**5;
LINELENGTH(40);                % 40 columns per line
TEST**5;
LINELENGTH();
LINELENGTH(80);
```

The output produced by Reduce may be written to external files. However, the file management depends on the operating system of the machine on which Reduce is running. Therefore, in addition to the Reduce commands which will be given below, additional commands, specific to the particular machine, may be necessary in order to make Reduce act in the way described.

To direct the output to be printed to an external file the OUT statement is used:

```
OUT filename;
```

Then the output is no longer directed to the terminal (or in batch mode to the standard output file), but to *filename* until the SHUT statement

```
    SHUT filename;
```

is issued or the session (or job) ends. If you want to re-use the output in a new session (or job) as input to Reduce, the output should be printed under control of `OFF ECHO;` and `OFF NAT;` (no natural output), as in the following example:

```
    OFF ECHO, NAT;
    OUT SAVEIT;
    TAYLOR(DF(SIN(X)**9,X,3),X,0,3);   % TAYLOR must have been defined
    SHUT SAVEIT;                       % close
    BYE;
```

The Taylor expansion will then be written to the file `SAVEIT` in Reduce input notation.

To read external files into Reduce, the statement

```
    IN filename;
```

must be used. The external files should always end with an `END` statement to avoid an error message:

$statement_1;$

$statement_2;$

.

.

$statement_n;$
```
;END;      % double semicolon to take care of unclosed expressions
```

If the `IN` statement that causes the reading in of the external file is terminated by a dollar sign rather than by a semicolon, the statements read in are not echoed at the terminal (or, in batch mode, on standard output).

6.6 Generating Fortran programs

A very useful feature is the printing of expressions and values in Fortran style, controlled by the switch

```
    ON FORT;   (default: off)
```

When `FORT` is turned on, every printed expression will begin in column 7, and, if extending over one line, a continuation mark will appear in column 6. The Reduce variable `!*CARDNO` specifies the maximum number of continuation lines and may be set to another value. If an expression would normally extend over this number of lines, a new expression is started. Expressions and strings are printed by the `WRITE` statement.

Example: Create a file containing a Fortran function that computes the Taylor expansion of *sin x*:

```
F:=TAYLOR(SIN X,X,0,5);
ON FORT;
OUT PROG;
WRITE "FUNCTION FUNC(X)";
WRITE FUNC:=F;
WRITE "RETURN";
WRITE "END";
SHUT PROG;
```

An extended package for creating Fortran programs, the GENTRAN package, is available in Reduce 3.3 (see the Reduce manual). Additional documentation for it is distributed with the Reduce installation tape.

6.7 Concluding remarks

In these lectures we have described the main functions and properties of Reduce. Nevertheless, a number of things had to be skipped. It is recommended that you read the manual and continue to practice programming with Reduce. If you are interested in the algorithms utilized by Reduce, ask your system manager for the Reduce source. Reduce is written in a Lisp dialect called RLISP. The complete source text is available to the users, but you need a good knowledge of programming Lisp in order to understand and possibly extend it.

6.8 Homework

- Verify Stirling's formula for the approximation of $n! \approx \sqrt{2n\pi}\, n^n e^{-n}$:
  - Show that $n! = \Gamma(n+1) := \int_0^\infty e^{-t} t^n dt$.
  - Compute the coordinate t_0 for which the integrand $e^{-t} t^n$ has its maximum.
  - Make a Taylor expansion of the logarithm of the integrand $e^{-t} t^n$, i.e., of $n \log t - t$ at t_0.
  - Substitute t by $t + t_0$ and integrate again. Remember $\int_0^\infty e^{-t^2/a} dt = \sqrt{\pi a}/2$.

- Verify that each product of two matrices of S_1 to S_6 belongs to S_1 to S_6. Build a product table.

$$S_1 = \begin{pmatrix} 1 & 0 & 0 \\ 0 & 1 & 0 \\ 0 & 0 & 1 \end{pmatrix}, \quad S_2 = \begin{pmatrix} 2 & -1 & -1 \\ 2 & -1 & -2 \\ 1 & -1 & 0 \end{pmatrix}, \quad S_3 = \begin{pmatrix} -1 & 4 & -5 \\ 0 & 1 & 0 \\ 0 & 0 & 1 \end{pmatrix},$$

$$S_4 = \begin{pmatrix} -2 & 7 & -11 \\ -2 & 7 & -12 \\ -1 & 3 & -5 \end{pmatrix}, \quad S_5 = \begin{pmatrix} 1 & 2 & -7 \\ 2 & -1 & -2 \\ 1 & -1 & 0 \end{pmatrix}, \quad S_6 = \begin{pmatrix} -1 & 6 & -12 \\ -2 & 7 & -12 \\ -1 & 3 & -5 \end{pmatrix}.$$

(See F. Neiss. Determinanten und Matrizen. Springer, Berlin, 1955.)

- For specialists in general relativity: Verify that the Kerr metric is a solution of Einstein's equation. If your program works, try the Kerr-Newman-NUT-deSitter metric, too. (See D. Kramer, H. Stephani, E. Herlt and M. MacCallum. Exact Solutions of Einstein's Field Equations. Deutscher Verlag der Wissenschaften, Berlin, 1980.)

- For a spherically symmetric and stationary spacetime in general relativity we have the following four Killing vectors:

$$_{(0)}\xi = e_t \,,$$

$$_{(1)}\xi = \sin\phi\, e_\theta + \cot\theta \cos\phi\, e_\phi \,,$$

$$_{(2)}\xi = -\cos\phi\, e_\theta + \cot\theta \sin\phi\, e_\phi \,,$$

$$_{(3)}\xi = e_\phi \,.$$

Prove that the Lie-derivatives $\mathcal{L}_{(i)\xi} F = 0$ for $i = 0, 1, 2, 3$, where F is the 2-form of the electromagnetic field of a point charge.

References

A.C. Hearn: "REDUCE User's Manual. Version 3.3". Rand Publication CP78 (Rev.7/87). The Rand Corporation, Santa Monica, CA 90406-2138, USA (1987).

B. Buchberger, G.E. Collins, and R.Loos (eds.):"Computer Algebra. Symbolic and Algebraic Computation." *Computing Supplementum 4.* Springer, Wien (1982).

G. Dautcourt, K.-P. Jann, E. Riemer and M. Riemer: "User's Guide to RE-DUCE Subroutines for Algebraic Computations in General Relativity." Astronomische Nachrichten **102** (1981) 1-13.

J.H. Davenport, Y. Siret, and E. Tournier: "Computer Algebra. Systems and algorithms for algebraic computation." Transl. from the French. Academic Press, London (1988).

D.G.B. Edelen: "Programs for computer implementation of the exterior calculus with applications to isovector calculations." Comp.& Maths. with Appls. **6** (1980) 415-424.

R. Esser, T. Pfenning, A. Strotmann, and V. Winkelmann: "REDUCE Version 3.2 Installation Guide for Control Data Cyber 170 Computers under NOS and NOS/BE". Arbeitsbericht RRZK-8609, Computer Center, University of Cologne (1986).

J. Fitch: "Solving Algebraic Problems with REDUCE." Journal of Symbolic Computation **1** (1985) 211-227.

R.A. d'Inverno:"A Review of Algebraic Computing in General Relativity." In *General Relativity and Gravitation. One Hundred Years after the Birth of Einstein.* A. Held, editor. Volume 1, pp.491-537. Plenum Press, NY (1980).

Y. Kanada: "REDUCE Programming, Vol.1." In Japanese. Computer Center, Tokyo University (1984).

A. Khuen: "Use of a Symbolic Algebra Program in NMR" (Nuclear Magnetic Resonance). Mikrochimica Acta (Wien) **1986 II**, 303-312.

M.A.H. MacCallum: "Algebraic Computing in General Relativity." In *Classical General Relativity, Proceedings of the Conference on Classical (Non-quantum) General Relativity, London.* Eds. W.B. Bonnor, J.N. Islam, and M.A.H. MacCallum, Cambridge Univ. Press, Cambridge, pp.145-171 (1984).

J.D. McCrea: "The Use of "REDUCE" in Finding Exact Solutions of the Quadratic Poincaré Gauge Field Equations". Ibid. pp.173-182.

A. Moussiaux, P.Tombal and J. Demaret: "Algebraic Programming of Hamiltonian Formalism in General Relativity: Application to Inhomogeneous Space-Times." General Relativity and Gravitation Journal **15** (1983) 209-226.

J.F. Ogilvie: "Computer algebra in modern physics." Computers in Physics **3** (1989) 66-74.

R. Pavelle, M. Rothstein and J. Fitch: "Computer Algebra". Scientific American **245** (Dec.1981) 136-152.

R. Pavelle: "MACSYMA from F to G." Journal of Symbolic Computation **1** (1985) 69-100.

G. Rayna: "REDUCE. Software for Algebraic Computation." Springer, New York (1987).

E. Schrüfer, F.W. Hehl, and J.D. McCrea: "Exterior Calculus on the Computer: The REDUCE–Package EXCALC Applied to General Relativity and to the Poincaré Gauge Theory". General Relativity and Gravitation Journal **19** (1987) 197-218.

F. Schwarz: "Algebraische Rechnungen in REDUCE". Lecture Notes. Universität Kaiserslautern (1981/82).

T. Wolf: "An Analytic Algorithm for Decoupling and Integrating Systems of Non-linear Partial Differential Equations". Journal of Computational Physics **60** (1985) 437-446.

C. Wooff and D. Hodgkinson: "muMATH: A microcomputer algebra system." Academic Press, London (1987).

Appendix

A.1 Where can you buy Reduce?

A Reduce information package is available from

• Dr. A.C. Hearn. The RAND Corporation, Santa Monica, CA 90406-2138, USA. Electronic mail (Arpanet) *reduce@rand.org* or (uucp) ... *!randvax!reduce* .

This information package describes how to obtain over twenty different versions of Reduce for about $500 each.

In particular, the Atari–Reduce based on Cambridge Lisp is available from

• Codemist Limited, "Alta", Horsecombe Vale, Combe Down, Bath, Avon BA2 5QR, England.

A.2 Some additional exercises (preliminary)

[1] The Bernoulli polynomials are defined by:

$$\frac{e^{xt}}{e^t - 1} = \sum_{n=1}^{\infty} B_n(x) \frac{t^{n-1}}{n!} .$$

-- Verify for $n = 1, 2, 3, 4, 5$:

$$B_n(x+1) - B_n(x) = nx .$$

— If $B_n := B_n(0)$ are the Bernoulli numbers, show:

$$x \coth x = 1 + \sum_{s=1}^{\infty} \frac{2^{2s} B_{2s}}{(2s)!} x^{2s} .$$

[2] Find a simple form of $df(x)/dx$ for the following functions $f(x)$:

$$sec(cos\, x), \qquad log\, \frac{\sqrt{1+x}}{(1-x)^{2/3}}, \qquad sin(abs\, x) .$$

(Recall that $sec\, x = 1/cos\, x$ and that $abs\, x$ denotes the absolute value of x.)

[3] Find the coefficient of x^3 in the Taylor series of $f(x) = e^{x+x^2}$.

[4] A few numerological exercises taken from some Newsletters of the Irish Mathematical Society:

— Find c, if a, b, and c are positive integers which satisfy $c = (a + bi)^3 - 107i$ and $i^2 = -1$.

— Assume that a, b, c, and d are positive integer such that $a^5 = b^4$, $c^3 = d^2$, and $c - a = 19$. Determine $d - b$.

— How long is the recurring block of digits in $(0.\overline{001})^2$?

— Consider the sequence of digits 198423768..., obtained by using the following rule: After 1984 every digit which appears is the final digit of the sum of the previous 4 digits. Does the grouping 1984 appear later in this sequence and, if so, when? What about the grouping 1985?

[5] Take the Pauli matrices σ_0, σ_1, σ_2, σ_3. Verify that the product of every two σ's is again, up to a factor, one of these matrices.

$$\sigma_0 = \begin{pmatrix} 1 & 0 \\ 0 & 1 \end{pmatrix}, \quad \sigma_1 = \begin{pmatrix} 0 & 1 \\ 1 & 0 \end{pmatrix}, \quad \sigma_2 = \begin{pmatrix} 0 & -i \\ i & 0 \end{pmatrix}, \quad \sigma_3 = \begin{pmatrix} 1 & 0 \\ 0 & -1 \end{pmatrix}.$$

For all $k, l = 0, 1, 2, 3$, compute the expressions

$$g_{kl} = \frac{1}{2}(\sigma_k \sigma_l + \sigma_l \sigma_k), \qquad a_{kl} = \frac{1}{2}(\sigma_k \sigma_l - \sigma_l \sigma_k).$$

[6] Let there be given the eight Gell–Mann matrices $\lambda_1, \lambda_2, \ldots \lambda_8$. They fulfill a number of simple relations

$$tr(\lambda_l) = 0, \quad tr(\lambda_k \lambda_l) = 2\delta_{kl}, \quad [\lambda_j \lambda_k] = 2i f_{jkl} \lambda_l.$$

Check these rules for the λ's as given below, and compute the structure constants f_{jkl}.

$$\lambda_1 = \begin{pmatrix} 0 & 1 & 0 \\ 1 & 0 & 0 \\ 0 & 0 & 0 \end{pmatrix}, \quad \lambda_2 = \begin{pmatrix} 0 & -i & 0 \\ i & 0 & 0 \\ 0 & 0 & 0 \end{pmatrix}, \quad \lambda_3 = \begin{pmatrix} 1 & 0 & 0 \\ 0 & -1 & 0 \\ 0 & 0 & 0 \end{pmatrix},$$

$$\lambda_4 = \begin{pmatrix} 0 & 0 & 1 \\ 0 & 0 & 0 \\ 1 & 0 & 0 \end{pmatrix}, \quad \lambda_5 = \begin{pmatrix} 0 & 0 & -i \\ 0 & 0 & 0 \\ i & 0 & 0 \end{pmatrix}, \quad \lambda_6 = \begin{pmatrix} 0 & 0 & 0 \\ 0 & 0 & 1 \\ 0 & 1 & 0 \end{pmatrix},$$

$$\lambda_7 = \begin{pmatrix} 0 & 0 & 0 \\ 0 & 0 & -i \\ 0 & i & 0 \end{pmatrix}, \quad \lambda_8 = \frac{1}{\sqrt{3}} \begin{pmatrix} 1 & 0 & 0 \\ 0 & 1 & 0 \\ 0 & 0 & -2 \end{pmatrix}.$$

(Note that we have $f_{jkl} = tr(\lambda_l [\lambda_j, \lambda_k])/(4i)$; compare C. Quigg: Gauge Theories of the Strong, Weak, and Electromagnetic Interactions. Page 196. Benjamin, Reading, 1983.)

[7] How many digits has the 100th member of the sequence 1, 1, 6, 12, 29, 59..., that is

$$x_n = x_{n-1} + 2x_{n-2} + n, \quad x_1 = x_2 = 1 ?$$

(See V.I. Arnol'd, Gewöhnliche Differentialgleichungen. P.268. Springer, Berlin (1980).

[8] Try to solve the second order modular equation

$$f(x) = \frac{2\sqrt{f(x^2)}}{1 + f(x^2)}.$$

See Scientific American, February 1988, page 68. We have still not looked for a solution. Perhaps you find one. Please let us know then (possibly via BITNET $\rightarrow$ ab047@dkOrrzkO).

[9] Evaluate some series for the computation of π. See Scientific American, February 1988, pages 66 to 73.

========
===

4. Appendix: A Short Introduction to FORTRAN (D.Stauffer)

So far, this book is unbalanced: The authors who need the computer to think have introduced the reader to the language REDUCE they use; but the two other authors who can already think and who use the computer for simulations have assumed that the reader understands FORTRAN, historically the first higher programmming language. A reader experienced in BASIC should be able to learn FORTRAN by simply reading the listed programs. True beginners may learn FORTRAN through the following remarks (the need for which was pointed out to us by J.Adler). Some statements are compared with the corresponding BASIC statements.

FORTRAN commands usually start in column 7 and end before column 73. A C in column 1 signifies a comment not to be executed by the computer, just like a REMark in BASIC. In column 6 we write a 1 if this line is a continuation of the command started in the previous line. In columns 2 to 5 we can give numbers as labels to mark certain lines (e.g. for GOTO commands); in contrast to BASIC not every line has to be numbered, and the numbers do not have to be ordered consecutively. Please distinguish carefully between the letter O and the number 0. The computer jumps to a line marked (in columns 2 to 5) by a 13 if it reads a command GOTO 13 somewhere else in the program.

Variables representing integers have a name starting with the letter I,J,K,L,M or N, like LSQ or K3; those representing a real number (floating point) start with other letters, like AREA or PMIN. Only short names (e.g., 5 characters; perhaps only 2 in BASIC) should be employed. The usual operations +, -, *, / (division) and ** (power) give real or integer results as is customary, except that division of one integer by another integer gives a rounded integer and not a real number. Thus ITIME- 10*(ITIME/10) is zero only if ITIME is an integer multiple of 10 (useful to limit printouts if ITIME runs from 1 to 100). Numbers without a decimal point, like 4, are integers, whereas those with a decimal point, like 4.0, are treated as real. With A = B4+CSQ the number stored currently under the name B4 is added to the number stored as CSQ, and this sum is stored in the memory cell denoted in the program as A. Thus K=K+1 is not a false mathematical assertion but a frequently used command for the computer to increase the current value of the variable K by one. After I = B4, the integer variable I contains only the rounded part of the real variable B4.

Mathematical functions are denoted as usual, e.g. SIN, COS, ABS, SQRT; but note ALOG for the natural logarithm, since LOG would be an integer. FLOAT(I) transforms the integer I into a real number, which is needed e.g. in square roots: A = SQRT(FLOAT(4)). IFIX(A) rounds the real number A into an integer and might also be called INT(A).

Decisions can be made automatically, like in

IF (A.GT.0) B = SQRT(A)

where .GT. stands for "greater than". (In BASIC we would write: IF A > 0 THEN B = SQR(A).) Similarly, the two letters LT (less than), GE (greater or equal), LE (less or equal), EQ (equal) and NE (not equal) must be enclosed by two dots. Such conditions can be inverted by .NOT. or combined by .AND. or by .OR., as in

IF(K.LT.1000.AND..NOT.(M.EQ.1000.OR.L.EQ.0)) GOTO 13

It makes little sense to ask IF(A.EQ.0) GOTO 13 since rounding errors could make the real number A different from zero; use ABS(A).LE.0.00001 instead.

Loops allow the repeated execution of a series of commands: With

```
      DO 99 K=M,N
      ...
      ...
99    CONTINUE
```

all commands written between the DO statement and the line with the label (as mentioned in the DO statement) are executed for all K values M, M+1, M+2, ..., N. (The upper limit N should not be smaller than the lower limit M.) The last line may also be a line which is executed for each K value; CONTINUE does nothing. In BASIC we would write: FOR K = M TO N as the first line, and NEXT K as the last line of the loop, with again all other commands in between. Double loops and more complicated nestings are allowed:

```
      DO 13 I=1,N
      DO 14 J=1,N
      ...

      ...
14    CONTINUE
      ...
13    CONTINUE
```

For the statements between label 14 and label 13 in this example, we only vary I whereas J is constant (presumably J=N+1).

Such loops are useful mainly in connection with arrays. With the definition

DIMENSION A(100,100), B(100), C(120)

at the beginning of the program, one treats the variable A as having two indices (subscripts), and B and C as having only one, with the indices running from 1 to 100 (to 120 for C). (BASIC abbreviates DIMENSION to DIM.) Then

```
      DO 2 I=1,N
      S=0.0
      DO 1 J=1,N
1     S=S+A(I,J)*B(J)
2     C(I)=S
```

gives the usual multiplication C = AB of a matrix A with a vector B: $C_I = \sum_J A_{IJ} B_J$ provided N is not larger than 100. (For N > 100 with the above dimensions the results can be completely crazy; if possible one should test a program by selecting a compiler option which checks wether or not the indices are within the defined bounds for each array. Only if tested successfully should one use the normal option of fast execution without such checks.) The above example also explains how one adds up; just remember the last time you checked out at the supermarket counter.

Results can be "printed out" on the standard printer (e.g. your screen) in a standard format by PRINT *, X,Y,K, while in BASIC we write PRINT X,Y,K. Arrays can be printed by suitable DO loops, or just by : PRINT *,C if the whole array C is needed. Input can be read in during program execution (details depend on your computer), written into the program (like N=50) or given at the beginning in a DATA statement like

DATA N,MAX,L,PI /50,1000,100,3.14159/

(Such DATA statements are short but dangerous: They are executed only once at the beginning of the program, and may lead to problems if used for large arrays as in DATA A /10000*1.0/ for a 100 * 100 matrix A.) BASIC usually does not have DATA statements.

If you submit your program to a big computer it will have to be preceded by control cards stating your user number, the Fortran compiler to be employed, and other details which one should copy from a working example of another user. The whole program often has to start with a line PROGRAM NAME, where NAME stands for the short name you want to give this program. Next follow the DIMENSION statements for the arrays, the DATA lines, and then the program itself. It ends with the line STOP (not needed for BASIC) followed by the line END, and perhaps some end-of-file mark, depending on your computer.